Revision and Practice in Mathematics

R. L. Bolt

Edward Arnold

© 1979 R. L. Bolt

First published 1979
by Edward Arnold (Publishers) Ltd.
41 Bedford Square, London WC1B 3DQ

Reprinted 1981, 1982

ISBN 0-7131 0335 3

Answers

Answers are published in a separate book.

Typeset by Reproduction Drawings Ltd., Sutton, Surrey.

Printed in Great Britain by
Spottiswoode Ballantyne Ltd.
Colchester and London

Contents

Number

The **natural numbers** are the counting numbers $1, 2, 3, 4, \ldots$.
The number 10 can be divided exactly by $1, 2, 5$ and 10. These are **factors** of 10.
A natural number which has no factors except 1 and itself is called a **prime number**. The first few prime numbers are $2, 3, 5, 7, 11, 13, 17, 19$. (1 is not considered to be a prime number.)
The **multiples** of 7 are $7, 14, 21, 28$, etc. 18 is a multiple of 2, of 3, of 9 and 18. Multiples of 5 end in 5 or 0.
Even numbers have 2 as a factor. They end in $0, 2, 4, 6$ or 8.
Odd numbers do not have 2 as a factor.
Index Form: $125 = 5 \times 5 \times 5 = 5^3$. The ^{3} is an index. (Plural: indices.)
Example: Express 24 and 245 as the product of prime numbers.

$24 = 8 \times 3 = 2 \times 2 \times 2 \times 3 = 2^3 \times 3$
$245 = 5 \times 49 = 5 \times 7 \times 7 = 5 \times 7^2$

The **integers** are $\ldots -5, -4, -3, -2, -1, 0, 1, 2, 3, 4, 5, \ldots$.
Rational numbers have the form p/q where p and q are integers ($q \neq 0$).

Examples are $\frac{2}{3}, -\frac{7}{19}, \frac{5}{1}, 0.63$ ($= \frac{63}{100}$).
Irrational numbers cannot be put in the form p/q. Examples are $\sqrt{2}, \sqrt[3]{5}, \pi$.

The rational numbers and the irrational numbers together form the set of **real numbers**.

Exercise 1

1. Which of the following numbers are even: $33, 48, 57, 61, 68, 78$?
2. Which of the numbers in question **1** are multiples of 3?
3. Which of the following have 7 as a factor: $91, 177, 154, 252, 648$?
4. Which of the following have 9 as a factor: $133, 139, 189, 288, 406$?
5. Which of the numbers between 20 and 40 have both 2 and 3 as factors?
6. List the prime numbers between 20 and 50.
7. List the prime numbers between 80 and 100.
8. Write in index form: $3 \times 3 \times 7 \times 7 \times 7, 2 \times 2 \times 2 \times 5, 5 \times 7 \times 7 \times 7 \times 7$.
9. What are the values of $3^2, 7^2, 2^3, 5^3, 2^5, 3^4, 1^5, 10^6$?
10. Work out the values of $2^3 \times 5, 3^2 \times 5, 2 \times 7^2, 2^4 \times 5^2, 3^2 \times 10^4$

11. List the factors of (a) 6 (b) 15 (c) 20 (d) 30 (e) 36
12. List the factors of 60. (a) Which are prime? (b) Repeat for 64.
13. List the factors of 24 and the factors of 30. (a) State the numbers which are factors of both 24 and 30. (b) Which is the largest? (This is the **Highest Common Factor** of 24 and 30.)
14. Repeat question 13 for (a) 60 and 75 (b) 128 and 144 (c) 160 and 224.
15. $90 = 2 \times 3^2 \times 5$. Express the following in this way: 18, 40, 100, 150, 189, 726, 808.
16. Write down the multiples of 5 up to 50 and the multiples of 3 up to 51. Which are multiples of both 5 and 3? Which is the smallest of these common multiples? This is the **Lowest Common Multiple** of 5 and 3.
17. Find the Lowest Common Multiple of (a) 3 and 7 (b) 10 and 15 (c) 18 and 21.
18. Which of the following numbers are (a) natural numbers (b) integers (c) rational numbers (d) irrational numbers:

    $\sqrt{3}, -62, 8, \sqrt{16}, 0.33, \frac{1}{3}, \pi, -\frac{6}{7}, \sqrt[3]{7}, 5.62$?

19. Copy the following sequences and add the next three terms to each:

    (a) $4, 7, 10, 13, \ldots$ (b) $3, 6, 12, 24, \ldots$
    (c) $15, 13, 11, 9, \ldots$ (d) $32, 16, 8, 4, \ldots$
    (e) $\frac{1}{2}, \frac{2}{3}, \frac{3}{4}, \frac{4}{5}, \ldots$ (f) $1, 4, 9, 16, \ldots$
    (g) $0, 1, 3, 6, 10, \ldots$ (h) $1, 1, 2, 3, 5, 8, \ldots$

Fractions

$\frac{2}{3}, \frac{4}{6}, \frac{6}{9}, \frac{8}{12}, \frac{10}{15}$ are all the same size. They are **equivalent fractions**.

$\frac{36}{45} = \frac{36 \div 9}{45 \div 9} = \frac{4}{5}$.

Here we have the equivalent fraction with the smallest **numerator** (top number) and **denominator** (bottom number). $\frac{36}{45}$ has been reduced to its lowest terms.

$3\frac{2}{5} = 3 + \frac{2}{5} = \frac{15}{5} + \frac{2}{5} = \frac{17}{5}$.

This is an **improper fraction**.

$\frac{38}{5} = \frac{35}{5} + \frac{3}{5} = 7\frac{3}{5}$.

This is a **mixed number**. The following examples show the methods of addition, subtraction, multiplication and division of fractions.

$1\frac{3}{4} + 3\frac{2}{3} = 1 + \frac{3}{4} + 3 + \frac{2}{3} = 4 + \frac{9}{12} + \frac{8}{12} = 4 + \frac{17}{12} = 4 + 1\frac{5}{12} = 5\frac{5}{12}$

$7\frac{1}{2} - 2\frac{4}{5} = 7 + \frac{1}{2} - 2 - \frac{4}{5} = 5 + \frac{5}{10} - \frac{8}{10} = 5 - \frac{3}{10} = 4\frac{7}{10}$

$\frac{2}{5} \times \frac{3}{4} = \frac{6}{20} = \frac{3}{10}$

$3\frac{2}{3} \times 1\frac{3}{4} = \frac{11}{3} \times \frac{7}{4} = \frac{77}{12} = 6\frac{5}{12}$

$4\frac{1}{5} \div 1\frac{1}{2} = \frac{21}{5} \div \frac{3}{2} = \frac{21}{5} \times \frac{2}{3} = \frac{42}{15} = \frac{14}{5} = 2\frac{4}{5}$

$2\frac{3}{4} \div 5 = \frac{11}{4} \div \frac{5}{1} = \frac{11}{4} \times \frac{1}{5} = \frac{11}{20}$

$\frac{2}{3}$ of $(\frac{4}{7} + \frac{1}{2}) = \frac{2}{3} \times (\frac{8}{14} + \frac{7}{14}) = \frac{2}{3} \times \frac{15}{14} = \frac{5}{7}$

Exercise 2

1. State the value of (a) $\frac{3}{4}$ hour (b) $\frac{5}{6}$ day (c) $\frac{2}{3}$ minute (d) $£\frac{3}{5}$
2. Write down three fractions which are equivalent to (a) $\frac{3}{4}$ (b) $\frac{2}{7}$
3. Which of the following fractions are equivalent to $\frac{2}{5}$:

   $\frac{6}{15}$, $\frac{14}{35}$, $\frac{4}{25}$, $\frac{10}{25}$, $\frac{18}{45}$?
4. Change to twentieths: $\frac{1}{2}$, $\frac{3}{4}$, $\frac{2}{5}$, $\frac{7}{10}$
5. Change $\frac{2}{3}, \frac{4}{9}$ and $\frac{5}{6}$ to eighteenths. Now write the original fractions in order of size with the largest first.
6. Change the following to twenty-fourths: $\frac{3}{4}$, $\frac{5}{8}$, $\frac{7}{12}$, $\frac{2}{3}$, $\frac{5}{6}$. Which is the largest of these fractions?
7. Arrange the following fractions in order of size with the smallest first:

   (a) $\frac{4}{7}$, $\frac{9}{14}$, $\frac{1}{2}$ (b) $\frac{1}{3}$, $\frac{2}{5}$, $\frac{3}{10}$, $\frac{4}{15}$
8. Reduce to their lowest terms: $\frac{8}{20}$, $\frac{15}{21}$, $\frac{49}{63}$, $\frac{125}{175}$

9. $\frac{2}{7} + \frac{3}{7}$ 10. $\frac{1}{3} + \frac{1}{2}$ 11. $\frac{4}{5} + \frac{3}{4}$ 12. $\frac{7}{9} - \frac{5}{9}$

13. $\frac{9}{10} - \frac{1}{5}$ 14. $\frac{3}{4} - \frac{1}{3}$ 15. $\frac{5}{6} - \frac{3}{8}$ 16. $\frac{4}{9} + \frac{11}{12}$

17. $1\frac{2}{3} + 1\frac{3}{4}$ 18. $1\frac{2}{7} + 2\frac{1}{3}$ 19. $1 - \frac{3}{7}$ 20. $4 - 1\frac{3}{4}$

21. $2\frac{3}{4} - 1\frac{1}{3}$ 22. $5\frac{2}{7} - 1\frac{9}{14}$ 23. $\frac{3}{7} \times \frac{2}{5}$ 24. $\frac{7}{9} \times \frac{3}{4}$

25. $1\frac{2}{5} \times 1\frac{1}{3}$ 26. $2\frac{1}{4} \times 5\frac{1}{3}$ 27. $6 \times 5\frac{1}{3}$ 28. $2\frac{2}{3} \times 3\frac{3}{4}$

29. $\frac{2}{7} \div \frac{3}{5}$ 30. $\frac{3}{5} \div \frac{2}{7}$ 31. $\frac{3}{5} \div 4$ 32. $4 \div \frac{3}{5}$

33. $1\frac{3}{4} \div 4\frac{1}{5}$ 34. $\frac{1}{3}$ of $\frac{6}{7}$ 35. $\frac{2}{5}$ of $3\frac{1}{3}$

36. $2\frac{4}{5} \times \frac{2}{7} \times 1\frac{1}{4}$ 37. $3\frac{1}{2} + 2\frac{1}{6} - 4\frac{2}{3}$ 38. $(\frac{3}{4} - \frac{1}{3}) \times \frac{2}{5}$

39. $(7\frac{5}{8} - 5\frac{3}{5}) \times 5\frac{1}{3}$ 40. $4\frac{2}{5} \div (\frac{1}{3} + \frac{2}{5})$ 41. $(\frac{4}{5} - \frac{3}{4}) \div \frac{7}{8}$

Decimals

$5.94 \times 10 = 59.4$; $0.76 \times 1000 = 760$

$0.03 \times 0.2 = 0.006$ [2 decimal places and 1 decimal place → 3 decimal places]

$2.25 \times 0.037 = 0.083\,25$ [2 decimal places and 3 decimal places → 5 decimal places]

$(0.4)^3 = 0.4 \times 0.4 \times 0.4 = 0.064$ [1 decimal place, 1 decimal place, 1 decimal place → 3 decimal places]

$63.7 \div 10 = 6.37$

$$2.73 \div 0.7 = \frac{2.73}{0.7} = \frac{2.73 \times 10}{0.7 \times 10} = \frac{27.3}{7} = 3.9$$

$$0.056 = \frac{56}{1000} = \frac{7}{125}; \quad \frac{9}{20} = \frac{9 \times 5}{20 \times 5} = \frac{45}{100} = 0.45$$

$\frac{3}{7} = 3 \div 7 = 0.4285\,714\,28\ldots = 0.\dot{4}2857\dot{1}$ a **recurring decimal**

$\frac{15}{23} = 15 \div 23 = 0.652$ correct to 3 decimal places [by division]

Approximation

Number	Correct to 3 dec. pl.	Correct to 2 dec. pl.	Correct to 1 dec. pl.
23.6934	23.693	23.69	23.7
0.4967	0.497	0.50	0.5

Number	Correct to 3 sig. fig.	Correct to 2 sig. fig.	Correct to 1 sig. fig.
4369	4370	4400	4000
8.026	8.03	8.0	8

If a distance is given as 9.3 km, correct to 2 significant figures, it is between 9.25 km and 9.35 km.

If a mass is given as 870 g, to 2 sig. fig., it is between 865 g and 875 g.

Exercise 3

No calculating aids should be used in this exercise.

Simplify:

1. $3.6 + 0.23$ 2. $8.04 + 7.3$ 3. $5.8 + 1.76$ 4. $5 - 0.27$
5. $6.4 - 0.08$ 6. $8.03 - 0.7$ 7. 6.83×10 8. 4.9×100
9. 0.27×1000 10. $3.8 \div 10$ 11. $0.63 \div 100$ 12. $49 \div 1000$
13. 0.6×0.04 14. 0.28×0.1 15. 0.09×0.007 16. $(0.3)^2$

17. $(0.5)^2$ **18.** $(0.09)^2$ **19.** 3.6×40 **20.** $3.6 \div 4$

21. $3.6 \div 40$ **22** $5.6 \div 0.7$ **23.** $5.6 \div 0.07$ **24.** $0.56 \div 0.7$

25. Give correct to 2 decimal places:
    5.628, 3.2296, 37.283, 0.0176, 0.0628

26. Give correct to 1 decimal place:
    3.784, 48.52, 0.716, 0.854, 0.0763

27. Give correct to 2 significant figures:
    639, 263, 0.0847, 0.0263, 5256

28. Give correct to 3 significant figures:
    3.517, 84 932, 60.46, 82.09, 0.04387

29. State the limits between which the following lengths lie:
    3.8 cm, 0.57 mm, 9.63 m, 0.059 mm

30. The following masses are given correct to 2 significant figures. Between what limits do they lie?
    76 g, 6.4 g, 83 g, 540 g, 9200 g, 300 g

31. Express as decimals: $\frac{3}{5}, \frac{7}{20}, \frac{3}{50}, \frac{21}{25}, \frac{9}{40}$.

32. Express each decimal number as a fraction with the numerator and denominator as small as possible: 0.8, 0.06, 0.35, 0.875, 0.048, 0.704

33. Express as decimals correct to 3 decimal places:
    $\frac{2}{3}, \frac{5}{7}, \frac{6}{11}, \frac{4}{9}, \frac{5}{12}, \frac{11}{17}, \frac{2}{53}$

34. Express as recurring decimals: $\frac{2}{3}, \frac{4}{9}, \frac{6}{11}, \frac{10}{11}, \frac{5}{7}$

Find the value of:

35. $\dfrac{0.7 \times 0.253}{0.11}$ **36.** $\dfrac{0.3 \times 0.42}{0.7}$ **37.** $\dfrac{60 \times (0.4)^2}{(0.2)^3}$

38. 4.6×2.7 **39.** 0.34×6.3 **40.** $(0.43)^2$

41. $9.88 \div 3.8$ **42.** $0.814 \div 0.74$ **43.** $24.94 \div 2.9$

Find, correct to 3 significant figures, the value of:

44. $8.2 \div 3.3$ **45.** $7.6 \div 0.052$ **46.** $0.76 \div 4.8$

47. Express in metres: 53 cm, 82 mm, 746 cm, 8 mm.

48. Express in kilograms: 36 g, 2400 g, 4 g, 380 g.

49. Express in metres: 3.7 km, 0.62 km, 80 mm, 5.9 cm.

50. Express as decimals of 1 hour, correct to 3 dec. pl.:
    29 minutes, 46 minutes, 2 minutes.

Squares, square roots and reciprocals

Squares

$(\frac{3}{4})^2 = \frac{3}{4} \times \frac{3}{4} = \frac{9}{16}$ $(2\frac{1}{3})^2 = (\frac{7}{3})^2 = \frac{7^2}{3^2} = \frac{49}{9} = 5\frac{4}{9}$

$120^2 = 120 \times 120 = 14\,400$ $472^2 = 472 \times 472 = 222\,784$

The square of a 3 digit integer is a 5 or 6 digit integer.

The square of an integer with n digits is an integer with $(2n-1)$ or $2n$ digits.

$0.003^2 = 0.003 \times 0.003 = 0.000\,009$ $0.068^2 = 0.068 \times 0.068 = 0.004\,624$

The square of a number with n decimal places is a number with $2n$ decimal places.

Exact square roots

$7^2 = 49$ and $(-7)^2 = 49$. 7 and -7 are the square roots of 49. We use $\sqrt{}$ for the positive square root.

$\sqrt{900} = 30$, $\sqrt{\frac{25}{36}} = \frac{\sqrt{25}}{\sqrt{36}} = \frac{5}{6}$, $\sqrt{7\frac{1}{9}} = \sqrt{\frac{64}{9}} = \frac{\sqrt{64}}{\sqrt{9}} = \frac{8}{3} = 2\frac{2}{3}$

The square root of an integer with $(2n-1)$ or $2n$ digits has n digits.

$\sqrt{25'00'00}$ (6 digits) $\sqrt{4'00'00}$ (5 digits)

$= \ 5 \quad 0 \quad 0$ (3 digits) $= 2 \quad 0 \quad 0$ (3 digits)

(In the given numbers the digits are paired from the decimal point.)

$\sqrt{0.00'00'64}$ (6 decimal places)

$= 0. \ 0 \quad 0 \quad 0$ (3 decimal places)

Approximate square roots can be obtained from tables or calculators

$\sqrt{6'21'00}$ $\sqrt{0.00'05'86}$

 2   4   9 .2   0. 0 2 4 2

Reciprocals

The reciprocal of n is $1/n$.

As $\frac{1}{5} = 0.2$, $\frac{1}{50} = 0.02$ and $\frac{1}{500} = 0.002$.

Also $\frac{1}{0.5} = \frac{10}{5} = 2$, $\frac{1}{0.05} = \frac{100}{5} = 20$ and $\frac{1}{0.005} = 200$.

The reciprocal of $\frac{2}{3}$ is $1/\frac{2}{3} = 1 \times \frac{3}{2} = 1\frac{1}{2}$.

Exercise 4

No calculating aids should be used in this exercise.

State the squares of:

1. 40   2. 300   3. 0.3   4. 0.4   5. 0.07

6. $\frac{1}{3}$ 7. $\frac{5}{6}$ 8. $\frac{2}{7}$ 9. -6 10. $-\frac{4}{9}$

Work out the squares of:

11. 0.15   12. 0.022   13. $3\frac{1}{2}$ 14. $1\frac{2}{3}$ 15. $-2\frac{3}{4}$

State the two square roots of:

16. 81   **17.** 100   **18.** 0.09   **19.** 0.64   **20.** $\frac{4}{9}$

Write down the value of:

21. $\sqrt{64}$ **22.** $\sqrt{400}$ **23.** $\sqrt{0.25}$ **24.** $\sqrt{0.0009}$ **25.** $\sqrt{\frac{16}{49}}$
26. $\sqrt{90000}$ **27.** $\sqrt{490\,000}$ **28.** $\sqrt{8100}$ **29.** $\sqrt{0.0049}$ **30.** $\sqrt{0.000\,081}$

Find the value of:

31. $\sqrt{1\frac{7}{9}}$ **32.** $\sqrt{12\frac{1}{4}}$ **33.** $\sqrt{7\frac{1}{9}}$ **34.** $\sqrt{1\frac{9}{16}}$ **35.** $\sqrt{1\frac{11}{25}}$

State, as exact decimals, the reciprocals of:

36. 2, 20 and 0.2 **37.** 10, 100 and 0.1   **38.** 4, 40 and 0.04
39. From the list of numbers below, select the approximate square roots of
(a) 33 (b) 3.3 (c) 69 (d) 6.9 (e) 0.45
List: 0.067, 0.21, 0.67, 1.8 2.6, 5.7, 8.3

Exercise 5

You may use any suitable calculating aid. Give your answers to 3 sig. fig.
Find the square of:

1. 5.28   **2.** 52.8   **3.** 0.528   **4.** 0.0528   **5.** 17.4
6. 470   **7.** 0.763   **8.** 0.0932   **9.** 0.318   **10.** 532.8

Find approximate values for the square roots of:

11. 7.2, 72, 720 and 7200   **12.** 3.3, 33, 330 and 3300
13. 23.8   **14.** 489   **15.** 3250   **16.** 0.19   **17.** 0.872
18. 0.000 283   **19.** 0.002 83   **20.** 363.5   **21.** 0.972   **22.** 8000

Find the reciprocals of:

23. 5.48, 548 and 0.548   **24.** 706, 70.6 and 0.0706
25. 1.837, 0.1837 and 183.7   **26.** 4832, 48 320 and 0.004 832
27. Find the value of $\frac{1}{12.7} + \frac{1}{25.9}$
28. Find the value of $\frac{1}{0.826} + \frac{1}{0.573}$

Indices and standard form

$a^3 \times a^2 = (a \times a \times a) \times (a \times a) = a \times a \times a \times a \times a = a^5 \quad (3 + 2 = 5)$

$b^6 \div b^4 = \dfrac{\not{b} \times \not{b} \times \not{b} \times \not{b} \times b \times b}{\not{b} \times \not{b} \times \not{b} \times \not{b}} = b \times b = b^2 \quad (6 - 4 = 2)$

$(c^2)^3 = (c \times c) \times (c \times c) \times (c \times c) = c \times c \times c \times c \times c \times c = c^6 \quad (2 \times 3 = 6)$

These are examples of the following rules:

$a^m \times a^n = a^{m+n}, a^m \div a^n = a^{m-n}, (a^m)^n = a^{mn}$

Negative indices: a^{-n} means $\dfrac{1}{a^n}$

7

Zero index: $a^0 = 1$

Examples:

$3^5 \times 3^2 = 3^{5+2} = 3^7$; $\quad 2^8 \div 2^5 = 2^{8-5} = 2^3 = 8$

$(7^3)^4 = 7^{3 \times 4} = 7^{12}$; $\quad 3^{-2} = \frac{1}{3^2} = \frac{1}{9}$

$2^5 \times 2^{-2} = 2^{5+(-2)} = 2^3 = 8$

Note: $5x^2$ means $5 \times x^2$ and NOT $(5x) \times (5x)$ which is $25x^2$.

Exercise 6

Find the value of:

1. 2^3 2. 3^4 3. 10^5 4. 5^3

5. $7^7 \div 7^5$ 6. $3^{10} \div 3^8$ 7. $5^9 \div 5^8$ 8. $10^{10} \div 10^7$

Simplify:

9. $a^5 \times a^4$ 10. $b^2 \times b^7$ 11. $c^{10} \div c^2$ 12. $d^9 \div d^3$

13. $(e^3)^5$ 14. $(f^4)^3$ 15. $g^2 \times g^3 \times g^4$ 16. $(h^5 \times h^4) \div h^3$

17. $(3a^2)^3$ 18. $(\frac{1}{3}b^3)^2$ 19. $(c^2 d)^4$ 20. $(e^5 f^2)^3$

21. If $n = 3$, find the value of n^2, $2n^2$ and $(2n)^2$.

22. If $h = \frac{1}{3}$, find the value of h^3, $6h^3$ and $(6h)^3$.

Find the value of:

23. 2^{-3} 24. 4^{-2} 25. 5^{-1} 26. 7^0

27. $3^4 \times 3^{-2}$ 28. $2^5 \times 2^{-6}$ 29. $2^2 \div 2^{-1}$ 30. $3^{-2} \div 3$

Simplify:

31. $a^5 \times a^{-2}$ 32. $b^3 \times b^{-7}$ 33. $c^2 \div c^{-3}$ 34. $d^{-2} \div d^3$

35. $e^{-5} \div e^{-8}$ 36. $(f^{-2})^{-3}$ 37. $(g^{-1})^4$ 38. $(h^2)^{-4}$

39. Express in the form 3^n: $9, 81, \frac{1}{9}, \frac{1}{3}, \frac{1}{27}$

40. Express in the form 10^p: $1000, \frac{1}{10}, 0.001, 0.00001$, 1 million

41. Express in the form 10^q: $10^2 \times 10^3$, 10×10^7, 10×10^{-3}, $10^5 \times 10^{-1}$, $(10^{-2})^3$

42. Express in the form 10^r: $10^4 \div 10$, $10^3 \div 10^4$, $10^{-2} \div 10^5$, $10^{-3} \div 10^{-7}$, $10^{-5} \div 10^{-1}$

43. Find the value of x if (a) $2^x = 64$ (b) $2^x = \frac{1}{8}$ (c) $10^x = 0.01$

44. Find the value of y if (a) $5^y = 1$ (b) $5^y = 625$ (c) $5^y = 0.04$

Standard form

Any positive number can be expressed in the form $a \times 10^n$ where $1 \leqslant a < 10$ and n is a positive or negative integer.

Examples:

$38\,400 = 3.84 \times 10000 = 3.84 \times 10^4$

$0.076 = \dfrac{76}{1000} = \dfrac{7.6}{100} = 7.6 \times \dfrac{1}{100} = 7.6 \times 10^{-2}$

Combining numbers in standard form:

$(8.2 \times 10^{-3}) + (4.7 \times 10^{-3}) = 12.9 \times 10^{-3}$

$(7 \times 10^5) \times (4 \times 10^3) = 28 \times 10^8 = 2.8 \times 10 \times 10^8 = 2.8 \times 10^9$

$(3.2 \times 10^2) \times (6 \times 10^{-5}) = 19.2 \times 10^{-3}$

$= 1.92 \times 10 \times 10^{-3} = 1.92 \times 10^{-2}$

$(2.2 \times 10^3) \div (5 \times 10^7) = 0.44 \times 10^{-4} = 4.4 \times 10^{-1} \times 10^{-4}$

$= 4.4 \times 10^{-5}$

$\sqrt{(9 \times 10^6)} = \sqrt{9} \times \sqrt{(10^6)} = 3 \times 10^3$

Exercise 7

Write the following numbers in standard form:
1. 830   2. 94 000   3. 5000   4. 205 000   5. 37.43
6. 0.0074   7. 0.823   8. 0.000 09   9. 0.000 604   10. 0.3
11. 4 million   12. 3 thousandths

Write as ordinary numbers, i.e. without powers of 10:
13. 5.8×10^2 14. 6.7×10^4 15. 8×10^3 16. 2.432×10^2
17. 9.3×10^{-2} 18. 4.5×10^{-4} 19. 3×10^{-3} 20. 2.83×10^{-1}

21. Explain why the following numbers are NOT in standard form:
23×10^4, 0.54×10^6, $7.6 \div 10^3$, $9.4 \times 10^{0.5}$

Do the following calculations, giving each answer in standard form:
22. $(3 \times 10) \times (2 \times 10^3)$ 23. $(5 \times 10^3) \times (7 \times 10^5)$
24. $(9 \times 10^4) \times (4 \times 10^2)$ 25. $(6 \times 10^5) \times (1.5 \times 10^2)$
26. $(1.5 \times 10) \times (8.8 \times 10^6)$ 27. $(8 \times 10^8) \div (4 \times 10^4)$
28. $(9.6 \times 10^{12}) \div (6 \times 10^5)$ 29. $(5.4 \times 10^5) \div (6 \times 10^2)$
30. $(3.6 \times 10^2) \div (9 \times 10^6)$ 31. $(4.2 \times 10^{-5}) \div (7 \times 10^2)$
32. $(2.4 \times 10^2) \div (4 \times 10^{-3})$ 33. $(0.06)^2$
34. $(6 \times 10^{-3})^2$ 35. $(4 \times 10^{-2}) \div (5 \times 10^{-5})$
36. $(3.75 \times 10^{-2}) \div (5 \times 10^{-6})$ 37. $\sqrt{(9 \times 10^8)}$
38. $\sqrt{(49 \times 10^{-6})}$
39. If $a = 9 \times 10^{-6}$ and $b = 4 \times 10^{-6}$, calculate $a + b$, $a - b$, $\sqrt{a}$, ab and $a \div b$.
40. If $h = 1.6 \times 10^5$ and $n = 4 \times 10^4$, calculate $h + n$, $h - n$, hn, $\sqrt{hn}$ and $h \div n$.

Ratio

$$850 \text{ g} : 2 \text{ kg} = \frac{850 \text{ g}}{2 \text{ kg}} = \frac{850 \text{ g}}{2000 \text{ g}} = \frac{85}{200} = \frac{17}{40} = 17 : 40$$

The plan of a room has a scale of 1 : 100. This means that each length on the plan is $\frac{1}{100}$ of the corresponding distance in the room. 7 m in the room is represented on the plan by $\frac{1}{100}$ of 7 m = $\frac{1}{100}$ of 700 cm = 7 cm.

To divide £30 between John and Mary in the ratio of 2 : 3, first divide it into 5 parts (2 + 3) and then give two parts to John and three to Mary.
$\frac{1}{5}$ of £30 = £6
So John has 2 × £6 = £12 and Mary has 3 × £6 = £18.

Exercise 8

Express the following ratios in their simplest forms:
1. 12 : 18   2. 28 : 24   3. 15 : 27   4. 35 : 25

5. $7 : 28$ 6. $54 : 9$ 7. $45 : 120$ 8. $280 : 420$
9. $60p : £1$ 10. $650\,g : 1\,kg$ 11. $900\,m : 1.4\,km$ 12. $2\,m : 360\,mm$
13. Two squares have sides of length 8 cm and 10 cm. Calculate the perimeter and area of each square. State in its simplest form, the ratio of (a) the sides (b) the perimeters (c) the areas.
14. A carpet is 9 m long and 6 m wide. State, in its simplest form, the ratio of (a) length to width (b) width to length.
15. Arrange the following numbers in pairs so that in each pair the ratio of the numbers is $2 : 5$:
4, 6, 8, 10, 12, 15, 18, 20, 30, 45
16. The scale of a plan of a room is $1 : 100$. What length on the plan represents (a) 400 cm (b) 3 m (c) 1.6 m in the room? What distance in the room is represented by (d) 3 cm (e) 2.7 cm (f) 8 mm?
17. On a $1 : 50\,000$ Ordnance Survey map (a) what distance in metres is represented by 1 mm? (b) what distance in kilometres is represented by 1 cm? (c) what distance in kilometres is represented by 4.6 cm? (d) what distance on the map represents 5.3 km?
   Divide the given number or quantity in the given ratio:
18. $35, 2 : 3$ 19. $40, 5 : 3$ 20. $80, 4 : 1$
21. $£4, 3 : 7$ 22. $7\,m, 1 : 4$ 23. $440\,cm, 8 : 3$
24. $£80, 2 : 3 : 5$ 25. $£4, 3 : 2 : 3$ 26. $3\,m, 3 : 4 : 5$
27. An alloy consists of 4 parts of one metal to 5 parts of another. How much of the first metal should be mixed with 40 kg of the second?
28. Two distances are in the ratio of $7 : 3$. If the first distance is 2.8 km, what is the second?
29. A photograph is enlarged in the ratio $9 : 2$. This means that the ratio of any length in the enlargement to the corresponding length in the original photograph is $9 : 2$. Find the sizes of a boat and a bridge in the enlargement if they were 8 mm and 36 mm in the original.
30. (a) Increase 30 cm in the ratio $6 : 5$.
   (b) Decrease 30 cm in the ratio $5 : 6$.
31. Express in the simplest form:
   (a) $2.5 : 4.5$ (b) $4\frac{1}{2} : 3\frac{1}{2}$ (c) $0.24 : 0.03$
32. Pete and Tony share a sum of money in the ratio $3 : 7$. Tony receives £12 more than Pete. How much does each receive?
33. Divide £10 in the ratio $4 : 3$ giving each part to the nearest penny.

Proportion and speeds

Exercise 9

1. An aircraft travels 72 kilometres in 8 minutes. At the same speed how far does it travel in (a) 1 minute (b) 15 minutes?
2. When 5 men shared a prize, each received £40. What was the prize? How much would 8 men get if they shared a prize of the same value?
3. A boy walked 504 metres in 6 minutes. Walking at the same speed, how far would he go in (a) 1 minute (b) 10 minutes?
4. A holiday camp has provisions for 28 children for 20 days. How long would the provisions last (a) 7 children (b) 70 children?
5. 300 metres of wire netting cost £14.70. Find the cost of 2 kilometres of such netting.
6. Andrew receives 76 French francs for £8. How much should Joan receive for £14?
7. Paul takes 124 steps in 100 metres. How many steps would he take in 350 metres? How far, to the nearest metre, would he go when taking 1000 steps?
8. A wheel of 20 teeth drives a second wheel of 30 teeth. If the speed of the first wheel is 48 revolutions per second, find the speed of the second wheel.

Speeds

$$\text{Average speed} = \frac{\text{distance travelled}}{\text{time taken}}.$$

Distance = speed × time.

$$\text{Time taken} = \frac{\text{distance}}{\text{speed}}$$

An aircraft travels 300 km in 25 minutes.

25 min = $\frac{5}{12}$ hour. The speed is $\frac{300}{5/12}$ km/h = $300 \times \frac{12}{5}$ km/h = 720 km/h

In $4\frac{1}{4}$ h it travels $720 \times 4\frac{1}{4}$ km = $720 \times \frac{17}{4}$ = 3060 km.

The time taken to travel 280 km = $\frac{280}{720}$ h = $\frac{280}{720} \times 60$ min = $23\frac{1}{3}$ min.

Note: 1 knot = 1 nautical mile per hour.

Exercise 10

1. For each of the following cases find the average speed in the units stated in brackets.
   (a) An aircraft travels 2590 kilometres in $3\frac{1}{2}$ hours (km/h)
   (b) A car travels 91 kilometres in 2 h 20 min. (km/h)
   (c) A boy runs 90 metres in 12 seconds. (m/s)
   (d) A boat travels 12 nautical miles in 45 minutes. (knots)

2. (a) Express a speed of 45 km/h in metres per second.
   (b) Express a speed of 15 m/s in kilometres per hour.
3. A racing car travelled 440 m in 8 s. Find its speed in km/h.
4. How long does it take an aircraft flying at 800 km/h to travel (a) 200 km (b) 360 km?
5. A boat has a speed of 18 km/h. How far does it go in (a) $3\frac{1}{2}$ h (b) 20 minutes?
6. An express train is travelling at 90 km/h. How far does it go in (a) 1 minute (b) 1 second?
7. An aircraft leaves London at 18.40 and arrives at Aberdeen at 20.35. If the distance is 660 km, calculate the speed to 3 sig. fig.
8. A sprinter runs 100 metres in 13.4 seconds. Find his average speed in km/h, correct to the nearest unit.
9. How long does it take a car travelling at 40 km/h to pass over a bridge of length 320 metres?
10. A car travels 50 km at 60 km/h and then 50 km at 40 km/h. Calculate (a) the time taken (b) the average speed.

Percentages

A **percentage** is a fraction with a denominator of 100.

3% means $\frac{3}{100}$ 100% is 1   50% is $\frac{1}{2}$ 10% is $\frac{1}{10}$

$45\% = \frac{45}{100} = \frac{9}{20}$ $17\frac{1}{2}\% = \frac{17\frac{1}{2}}{100} = \frac{35}{200} = \frac{7}{40}$ $8.3\% = \frac{8.3}{100} = \frac{83}{1000} = 0.083$

Thus, to convert a percentage to a fraction or decimal, we divide by 100. Reversing this, we change a fraction or decimal into a percentage by multiplying by 100.

$\frac{7}{20} = \frac{700}{20}\% = 35\%$ $0.046 = 0.046 \times 100\% = 4.6\%$

$\frac{5}{6} = \frac{500}{6}\% = 83\frac{1}{3}\%$

$15\% \text{ of } £4.40 = \dfrac{15}{100} \text{ of } 440\text{p} = \dfrac{15 \times 440}{100}\text{p} = 66\text{p}$

Example: Express £1.65 as a percentage of £3.75

$\dfrac{£1.65}{£3.75} = \dfrac{165\text{p}}{375\text{p}} = \dfrac{33}{75} = \dfrac{11}{25} = \dfrac{11 \times 100}{25}\% = 44\%$

Profit (or Loss) per cent $= \dfrac{\text{profit (or loss)}}{\text{cost price}} \times \dfrac{100}{1}\%$

Example: A dealer buys a car for £1280 and sells it for £1632. Find his profit per cent.

profit = selling price − cost price = £1632 − £1280 = £352

$$\text{profit \%} = \frac{352}{1280} \times \frac{100}{1}\% = \frac{55}{2}\% = 27\tfrac{1}{2}\%$$

Example: A radio is sold for £28 thereby making a profit of 12% of the cost price. Find the cost price.

selling price = cost price + profit
            = cost price + 12% of cost price
            = 112% of cost price
112% of cost price = £28
100% of cost price = £28 × $\frac{100}{112}$ = £25

Exercise 11

1. Express as fractions in their lowest terms and as decimals:
   65%, 24%, 70%, 75%, 62$\frac{1}{2}$%, 18$\frac{3}{4}$%
2. Express as percentages: $\frac{17}{20}, \frac{1}{4}, \frac{9}{25}, \frac{33}{50}, 0.8, 0.74$
3. Express as percentages: $\frac{1}{6}, \frac{2}{3}, \frac{4}{7}, 0.275, 0.085, 0.317$
   Find the value of:
4. 35% of £80   5. 85% of 1 kg   6. 68% of £15
7. 3% of £17   8. 7$\frac{1}{2}$% of £4.20   9. 16% of 3650 g
   Express the first quantity as a percentage of the second:
10. £1.40, £2   11. £4.20, £7.50
12. 54 minutes, 2 hours   13. 234 g, 4.5 kg
14. A bill for £280 is reduced by 15% discount. What sum should be paid?
15. A candidate in an examination obtained 68 marks out of 80 on one paper and 114 out of 150 on another. Express each score as a percentage of the possible score and say which is the higher.
16. A man earning £120 per week has a 7% rise. Find his new wage.
17. £724 is invested in a building society paying 6$\frac{1}{2}$% interest per year. How much interest is received after a year?
18. A man bought a car for £3200. After one year it was worth £2640. Express the fall in value as a percentage of the price paid.
19. 14% of a sum of money is £126. What is 1%? What is the whole sum?
20. 60% of a sum of money is £22.80. What is 10%? What is the whole sum?
    Copy and complete the following:

	Cost Price	Selling Price	Profit or Loss	Profit or Loss %
21.	£48	£84		
22.	£660			35% profit
23.	£7.50	£6		
24.		£682		24% profit
25.		£101.50		16% profit

26. A shop allows a discount of 10% on all bills during its 'Bargain Week'. What was the original amount of a bill which was settled for £35.10?
27. A greengrocer bought 150 oranges for £4.80 and sold them at 5p each. Find his percentage profit on outlay.

Areas and perimeters

Areas

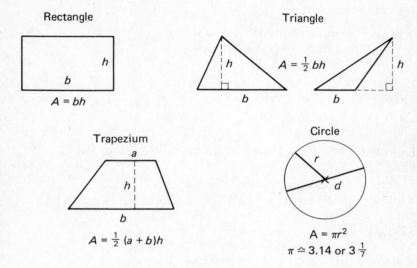

Rectangle

$A = bh$

Triangle

$A = \frac{1}{2} bh$

Trapezium

$A = \frac{1}{2} (a + b)h$

Circle

$A = \pi r^2$

$\pi \simeq 3.14$ or $3\frac{1}{7}$

Fig. 1

The **perimeter** of a figure is the distance round it.
The perimeter of a rectangle is $2b + 2h$.
The perimeter (or **circumference**) of a circle is πd or $2\pi r$

Example 1: The area of a triangle is 8.4 cm². Its base is 4.8 cm. Find its height.

$$\frac{1}{2}bh = A$$
$$\frac{1}{2} \times 4.8 \times h = 8.4$$
$$2.4 \times h = 8.4$$
$$h = \frac{8.4}{2.4} = \frac{84}{24} = \frac{7}{2} = 3.5 \text{ cm}$$

Example 2: Find the perimeter and area of a sector of a circle of radius 9.3 cm if the angle at the centre is 50°.

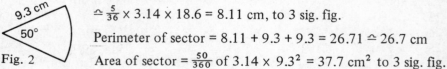

9.3 cm

50°

Fig. 2

Circumference of circle $= \pi \times 18.6$ cm

Length of arc of sector $= \frac{50}{360}$ of $\pi \times 18.6$ cm

$\simeq \frac{5}{36} \times 3.14 \times 18.6 = 8.11$ cm, to 3 sig. fig.

Perimeter of sector $= 8.11 + 9.3 + 9.3 = 26.71 \simeq 26.7$ cm

Area of sector $= \frac{50}{360}$ of $3.14 \times 9.3^2 = 37.7$ cm² to 3 sig. fig.

14

Exercise 12

1. Copy and complete the following table for rectangles:

	Base	Height	Perimeter	Area
(a)	8 cm	6 cm		
(b)	10 cm			70 cm²
(c)	9 cm		24 cm	
(d)	7.2 cm	5.5 cm		

2. Calculate the area of a triangle having base and height of (a) 9 cm and 8 cm (b) 15 cm and 10 cm (c) 8.8 cm and 5.5 cm.
3. (a) A square has a side of 9 cm. State its area and perimeter.
   (b) A square has a perimeter of 28 cm. State its area.
4. A picture of length 25 cm and height 18 cm is mounted on a card of length 32 cm and height 24 cm. Calculate the area of (a) the picture (b) the whole card (c) the border outside the picture.
5. A rectangular pond of length 12 m and breadth 8 m is surrounded by a path of width 1 m. Calculate the area of the path.
6. How many square linoleum tiles of side 20 cm are needed to cover a floor 4.6 m by 3.4 m?
7. Find the area of a trapezium of height 8 cm with parallel sides of length 10 cm and 14 cm.
8. Calculate the height of a triangle having a base of 14 cm and area of 56 cm².
9. Calculate the base of a triangle of height 7.5 cm and area 48 cm².
10. Find, to 2 sig. fig., the circumference of a circle of radius (a) 6 cm (b) 2.8 m. Take π as 3.14.
11. A car tyre has a radius of 28 cm. Using $3\frac{1}{7}$ for π, find (a) its circumference (b) the number of revolutions it makes in 5.5 km.
12. A running track has two semi-circular ends of radius 63 m and two equal straight parts. The perimeter of the track is 1000 m. Using $3\frac{1}{7}$ for π, calculate the length of (a) each semi-circle (b) each straight part.
13. Using $3\frac{1}{7}$ for π, calculate the diameter of a circle of circumference (a) 44 cm (b) 143 cm.
14. Calculate, to 2 sig. fig., the diameter of a circle of circumference 27 cm. Use 3.14 for π.
15. Calculate, to 2 sig. fig., the area of a circle of radius (a) 7 cm (b) 5.6 m. Take π as $3\frac{1}{7}$.
16. Calculate the area of a circle of radius (a) 9 cm (b) 4.7 m.
17. A circular fish pond of diameter 26 m is surrounded by a concrete path of width 2 m. Find the area of the path. Use $3\frac{1}{7}$ for π.
18. There are 120 turns of wire on a cylinder of radius 2 cm. Find the length of the wire, correct to the nearest 10 cm. Use 3.14 for π.

15

19. C is the centre of a circle of radius 7 cm. A and B are points on the circumference. Calculate the length of arc AB if A$\hat{\text{C}}$B is (a) 90° (b) 120° (c) 135°. Take π as $3\frac{1}{7}$.

20. For the circle of question **19**. Calculate the area of the sector ACB in each case.

21. Using 3.14 for π, calculate (a) the perimeter (b) the area of a sector of angle 110° and radius 9.6 cm.

Pythagoras' theorem

In Fig. 1, $a^2 = b^2 + c^2$

Exercise 13

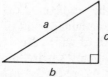
Fig. 1

1. If $b = 6$ and $c = 8$, calculate a.

2. If $b = 24$ and $c = 7$, calculate a.

3. If $b = 5$ and $a = 13$, calculate c.

4. If $a = 17$ and $c = 15$, calculate b.

5. If $b = 4.5$ and $c = 2.8$, calculate a.

6. If $b = 23$ and $c = 38$, calculate a, correct to 3 sig. fig.

7. If $a = 5.2$ and $c = 3.4$, calculate b, correct to 3 sig. fig.

8. In triangle DEF, $\hat{\text{D}} = 90°$, DE = 9 cm and DF = 12 cm. Calculate EF.

9. In triangle GHK, $\hat{\text{H}} = 90°$. GK = 11 cm and HK = 6 cm. Calculate GH.

10. In Fig. 2, PQ = PR = 10 cm and QR = 12 cm. State the length of QN. Calculate the length of PN and the area of the triangle.

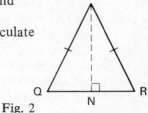
Fig. 2

11. In Fig. 2, PQ = PR = 7 cm and QR = 6 cm. Calculate PN, correct to 2 sig. fig.

12. Calculate, correct to 2 sig. fig. the length of a diagonal of a square of side 6 cm.

13. A rectangle has sides of 5.5 cm and 4.8 cm. Calculate the length of a diagonal.

14. A football pitch has been marked out with sides of 120 m and 90 m. In order to check that it is a rectangle, the diagonals are measured. How long should they be?

15. In a diagram show the points A (4, 6) and B (8, 9) and calculate the length of AB.

16. In a diagram show the points C (3, 1) and D (−4, 6). Calculate CD, correct to 2 sig. fig.

17. A rhombus has sides of length 13 cm and one diagonal of length 10 cm. Calculate the length of the other.

16

18. A boat sails 20 nautical miles due east and then 14 nautical miles due south. How far is it from its starting point, correct to 3 sig. fig.?
19. An equilateral triangle has sides of 9 cm. Calculate the length of an altitude, correct to 2 sig. fig.

Volumes and surface areas

Cuboid or rectangular prism

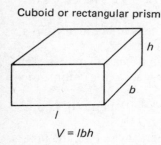

$V = lbh$

Cylinder

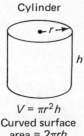

$V = \pi r^2 h$

Curved surface area $= 2\pi rh$

Prism (on any base)

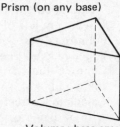

Volume: base area x height

Fig. 1

Exercise 14

1. Find the volume of a cuboid (a) 8 cm by 5 cm by 4 cm (b) 10 cm by 7 cm by 6 cm (c) 7.2 cm by 6.5 cm by 5 cm.
2. Find the total surface areas of the cuboids in question 1 (a) and (b).
3. How many cubes of edge 2 cm can be fitted into a box 12 cm by 8 cm by 6 cm?
4. A cuboid has a length of 8 cm, a breadth of 5 cm and a volume of 280 cm^3. Calculate its height.
5. A cuboid has a square base, a height of 15 cm and a volume of 540 cm^3. Find the length of a side of the square base.
6. The total surface area of a cube is 150 cm^2. Find (a) the area of each face (b) the length of each edge (c) the volume.
7. A glass tank is 40 cm long, 30 cm wide and 20 cm high. Calculate its volume (a) in cm^3 (b) in ml (c) in litres.
8. A room is 640 cm by 500 cm by 350 cm. Find its volume in cubic metres.
9. 21 litres of water are poured into a fish tank of length 60 cm and width 35 cm. Calculate the depth of the water.
10. Some cubes of edge 3 cm were lowered into a tank full of water and 216 ml overflowed. How many cubes were placed in the tank?

17

11. Calculate the volume of a block of lead 30 cm by 24 cm by 15 cm. If the block is hammered out to make a square plate of thickness 3 cm, what is the width of the square?

12. Water is flowing into a rectangular tank of length 50 cm and width 40 cm at the rate of 120 cm^3 per second. Find the rise in the level in 5 minutes.

Find the volume and the area of the curved surface for a cylinder having the given dimensions:

13. Radius 7 cm, height 5 cm ($3\frac{1}{7}$)   14. Diameter 60 cm, height 21 cm ($3\frac{1}{7}$)

15. Radius 1.3 m, height 1.5 m (3.14) 16. Diameter 4.6 cm, height 1.3 m (3.14)

17. A cylinder has a radius of 14 cm. Using $3\frac{1}{7}$ for π, calculate the area of one end. If the volume is 9240 cm^3, calculate the height.

18. 3.85 litres of water are poured into a cylinder having a base radius of 7 cm. Calculate the height of the water (Use $3\frac{1}{7}$ for π).

19. How many jars of diameter 6 cm and height 8 cm can be filled from a cylindrical vessel of diameter 48 cm and height 36 cm?

20. A pencil has a diameter of 6 mm and the lead in it has a diameter of 2 mm. Calculate the ratio of the volume of the lead to the volume of the wood.

21. Calculate, correct to the nearest gram the mass of 10 metres of copper wire of diameter 2 mm if the mass of 1 cm^3 is 8.93 g.

22. A pipe has a cross sectional area of 5 cm^2. Water flows along the pipe at 0.8 m per sec. How many litres of water leave the pipe each minute?

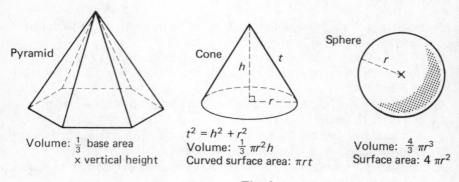

Pyramid

Volume: $\frac{1}{3}$ base area x vertical height

Cone

$t^2 = h^2 + r^2$
Volume: $\frac{1}{3}\pi r^2 h$
Curved surface area: $\pi r t$

Sphere

Volume: $\frac{4}{3}\pi r^3$
Surface area: $4\pi r^2$

Fig. 2

Example: A cone has a height of 12 cm and a base radius of 5 cm. Calculate
(a) its slant height (b) its total surface area (c) its volume.
(a) $t^2 = h^2 + r^2 = 144 + 25 = 169$. $t = 13$.
   The slant height is 13 cm.
(b) Curved surface area $= \pi r t \approx 3.14 \times 5 \times 13 = 204.1$ cm^2
   Area of base $= \pi r^2 \approx 3.14 \times 25 = 78.5$ cm^2
   Total surface area $= 204.1 + 78.5 = 282.6$ cm$^2 = 283$ cm^2, to 3 sig. fig.
(c) Volume $= \frac{1}{3}\pi r^2 h = \frac{1}{3} \times 3.14 \times 25 \times 12 = 314$ cm^3

18

Exercise 15

1. Calculate the volume of a pyramid having (a) height 18 cm and a square base of side 10 cm. (b) height 20 cm and a rectangular base 12.5 cm by 8.7 cm. (c) height 9 cm and a triangular base with sides of 5 cm and 8 cm and an angle of 90° between them.
2. A pyramid has a rectangular base 10 cm by 9 cm and a volume of 360 cm^3. Calculate its height.
3. Draw the net for a pyramid having a square base of side 16 cm and each of the four faces as isosceles triangles with sides of 17 cm, 17 cm and 16 cm. Calculate the area of each triangular face and hence the area of the surface of the pyramid.
4. Using $3\frac{1}{7}$ for π, calculate the volume of a cone with (a) radius 14 cm and vertical height 15 cm (b) radius 35 cm and vertical height 12 cm.
5. Using 3.14 for π, calculate, correct to 3 sig. fig., the volume of a cone with (a) radius 5 cm and vertical height 9 cm (b) radius 62 mm and vertical height 152 mm.
6. A cone has a base radius of 7 cm and a vertical height of 24 cm. Using $3\frac{1}{7}$ for π, calculate (a) the slant height (b) the curved surface area.
7. A cone has a slant height of 65 cm and a base radius of 16 cm. Calculate (a) the vertical height (b) the volume. Use $3\frac{1}{7}$ for π.
8. Calculate the surface area of a sphere of radius (a) 7 cm (b) 14 cm. Take π as $3\frac{1}{7}$.
9. Calculate the volume of a sphere of radius 21 cm. Take π as $3\frac{1}{7}$.
10. Calculate, correct to 3 sig. fig., the volume and surface area of a sphere of radius 6.8 cm, using 3.14 for π.
11. Calculate, correct to 3 sig. fig., the volume of metal required to make 10 000 ball bearings of diameter 4 cm.

Number bases

Just as the denary number 2345_{10} means $2 \times 10^3 + 3 \times 10^2 + 4 \times 10^1 + 5$ so the base eight number 2345_8 means $2 \times 8^3 + 3 \times 8^2 + 4 \times 8^1 + 5$ which is $2 \times 512_{10} + 3 \times 64_{10} + 4 \times 8 + 5 = 1253_{10}$

Binary numbers are based on the number two.

$101101_2 = 1 \times 2^5 + 0 \times 2^4 + 1 \times 2^3 + 1 \times 2^2 + 0 \times 2^1 + 1$
$= 32_{10} + 0 + 8 + 4 + 0 + 1 = 45_{10}$

427_{10} can be converted to base eight by repeated division by 8.

$$8 \overline{)\ 427 \text{ units}}$$
$$8 \overline{)\ 53 \text{ eights 3 units}}$$
$$6 \text{ sixty-fours 5 eights 3 units}$$
$$427_{10} = 653_8$$

Exercise 16

1. Express as denary (base 10) numbers:
   (a) 16_8 (b) 55_8 (c) 120_8 (d) 364_8
2. Express as denary numbers:
   (a) 22_4 (b) 102_3 (c) 431_5 (d) 1101_2
3. Express the following denary numbers as base eight numbers:
   (a) 13 (b) 42 (c) 395 (d) 629
4. Express the following denary numbers as binary numbers:
   (a) 6 (b) 14 (c) 27 (d) 45
5. Express the number 18_{10} in the following scales:
   (a) 8 (b) 5 (c) 3 (d) 2
6. Write out the first sixteen numbers in the scale of
   (a) 3 (b) 5 (c) 7 (d) 2
7. State the largest denary number which can be represented by four digits (a) in the binary scale (b) in the scale of 4.
8. Write out the addition table for the scale of (a) 3 (b) 4 (c) 5
9. Write out the multiplication table for the scale of
   (a) 3 (b) 4 (c) 5.
10. Use one of the tables of question 9 to calculate
    (a) $13_4 \times 23_4$ (b) $322_4 \times 32_4$
    Work out in base 2 (binary):
11. (a) $11 + 1$ (b) $110 + 101$ (c) $101 + 111$
12. (a) $100 - 1$ (b) $1101 - 10$ (c) $1010 - 111$
13. (a) 110×11 (b) 1011×110 (c) 1101×101
14. (a) $1111 \div 11$ (b) $1\,000\,001 \div 101$
15. (a) $11\,011 + 11\,011$ (b) $11\,011 \times 10$
16. How can you tell whether or not a binary number is a multiple of
    (a) two (b) four (c) eight?
17. Carry out the following calculations in base 3:
    (a) $22 + 1$ (b) $112 + 121$ (c) $200 - 12$
18. Carry out the following calculations in base 4:
    (a) $23 + 22$ (b) $100 - 32$ (c) $230 - 33$
19. Work out $25_8 + 74_8$, giving your answer in base 8.
20. State the number base for each of the following:
    (a) $211 - 133 = 23$ (b) $7 \times 7 = 54$ (c) $44 \times 4 = 220$
21. $x_{10} = 13_n$ where $1 < x < 10$. Find three possible values of x and the corresponding values of n.

Sets

Take the universal (or background) set, ξ, as {natural numbers < 10} so that $\xi = \{1, 2, 3, 4, \ldots 9\}$.

Let D = {odd numbers} = $\{1, 3, 5, 7, 9\}$, T = {multiples of 3} = $\{3, 6, 9\}$ and H = $\{5, 9\}$.

$7 \in D$ means that 7 is an element of the set D.

$8 \notin D$ means that 8 is not an element of the set D.

$H \subset D$ means that H is a subset of D.

$D \supset H$ means that D contains H as a subset.

D', the complement of D, is $\{2, 4, 6, 8,\}$. It consists of the elements of ξ which are not elements of D.

$D \cap T$, the intersection of D and T is $\{3, 9\}$. It contains those elements which are in both D and T.

$D \cup T$, the union of D and T, is $\{1, 3, 5, 6, 7, 9\}$. It contains all the elements of D and all the elements of T.

The empty set has no elements. It is denoted by ϕ or {   }.

$n(D)$ means the number of elements in set D. Thus $n(D) = 5$.

If $E = \{x : x > 6\}$, then $E = \{7, 8, 9\}$.

Fig. 1 is a Venn diagram for the sets ξ, D and T.

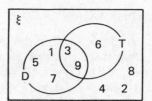

Fig. 1

Exercise 17

1. P = $\{a, c, d, e\}$, Q = $\{c, e, f\}$, R = $\{a, e, f, g\}$.
   List (a) $P \cap Q$ (b) $Q \cap R$ (c) $P \cap Q \cap R$ (d) $P \cup Q$ (e) $P \cup Q \cup R$.
2. A = $\{4, 5, 6, 7, 8\}$, B = $\{6, 7, 8, 9\}$, C = $\{4, 6, 8, 9\}$.
   List (a) $A \cap B$ (b) $A \cap B \cap C$ (c) $A \cup C$ (d) $A \cup B \cup C$.
3. $\xi = \{m, p, q, r, t, y\}$, K = $\{p, r, t\}$, G = $\{r, y\}$.
   List $K \cap G$. Draw a Venn diagram and enter all the elements.
   List K', G' and $K' \cap G'$.
4. $\xi = \{a, b, c, d, e, f\}$, H = $\{b, d, f\}$, N = $\{a, e\}$.
   Comment on $H \cap N$. Show the sets in a Venn diagram. List (a) H'
   (b) N' (c) $H \cap N'$ (d) $H' \cap N$ (e) $H' \cap N'$
5. $\xi = \{$whole numbers $< 10\}$, V = {even numbers}, F = {multiples of 4}. Draw a Venn diagram and place all the elements in the correct parts. List V'. Comment on $V \cap F$.
6. Make five copies of Fig. 2 and use them to show by shading (a) $A \cap B$ (b) $A \cup B$ (c) A' (d) $A' \cap B'$ (e) $A' \cup B'$

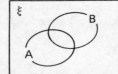

Fig. 2

21

7. Make five copies of Fig. 3 and use them to show by shading (a) $C \cap D$ (b) $C \cup D$ (c) C' (d) $C' \cap D'$ (e) $C' \cup D'$

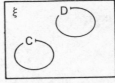

Fig. 3

8. Make five copies of Fig. 4 and use them to show by shading (a) $F \cap G$ (b) $F \cup G$ (c) F' (d) $F' \cap G'$ (e) $F' \cup G'$

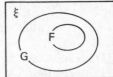

Fig. 4

9. $\xi = \{11, 12, 13, \ldots 19\}$. $A = \{x : x \text{ is an even number}\}$, $B = \{x : x \text{ is a multiple of } 3\}$, $C = \{x : x \text{ is a prime number}\}$. List A, B, C and $A \cap B$. Comment on $A \cap C$ and $B \cap C$. Show ξ, A, B and C in a Venn diagram.

10. $\xi = \{a, b, c, d, e\}$, $P = \{a, c, e\}$, $Q = \{a, b, c\}$, $R = \{b, d\}$, $S = \{e\}$. Copy and complete (a) $P \cap \ldots = \phi$ (b) $R \cup \ldots = S'$ (c) $Q \cap \ldots = (R \cup S)'$

11. $A = \{0, 1\}$. List the subsets of A. (We include ϕ and A itself as subsets of A). How many are there? Repeat for $B = \{0, 1, 2\}$. How many subsets has $\{0, 1, 2, 3\}$?

Exercise 18

1. In Fig. 5, the 7 in the section $P \cap Q$ means that there are seven elements in that section, i.e. $n(P \cap Q) = 7$. Similarly $n(P) = 3 + 7 = 10$. State $n(Q)$, $n(\xi)$, $n(P \cup Q)$, $n(P')$, $n(Q')$, $n(P \cap Q')$ and $n(P' \cap Q')$.

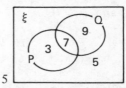

Fig. 5

2. Make a copy of Fig. 2. Enter numbers as in Fig. 5 so that $n(A \cap B) = 4$, $n(A) = 12$, $n(B) = 10$ and $n(\xi) = 27$.
State $n(A')$, $n(B')$, $n(A \cup B)$ and $n(A' \cap B)$.

3. (a) D and E are two sets. $n(D) = 12$, $n(E) = 9$ and $n(D \cap E) = 4$. Find $n(D \cup E)$. A Venn diagram may help you.
(b) F and G are two sets. $n(F) = 17$, $n(F \cap G) = 9$, $n(F \cup G) = 20$. Find $n(G)$.

4. In a class of 25 pupils, 10 have dogs, 7 have cats and 5 have both. Taking ξ, D and C as the sets, draw a Venn diagram like Fig. 5 and from it state the number who (a) have neither dogs nor cats (b) cats but not dogs.

5. 29 pupils in a class sat a Mathematics examination and an English examination. 7 failed both, 13 passed in Mathematics and 17 passed in English. Using a Venn diagram, find (a) the number who passed Mathematics but failed English (b) the number who passed both.

6. Of 50 passengers leaving a train, 19 carried luggage in the left hand,

22

34 carried luggage in the right hand and 9 had no luggage. How many carried luggage in both hands?

7. Three Mathematics tests, A, B and C, were given to a class of 30 pupils. 17 passed A, 18 passed B, 14 passed C; 12 passed both A and B, 10 passed both B and C, 11 passed both C and A and 8 passed all three. Using a Venn diagram with three overlapping sets in a universal set, find how many passed (a) none of the tests (b) only A (c) B and C but not A.

Directed numbers and substitution

Directed Numbers

Adding: $(-8) + (-3) = (-11)$, $(-8) + 3 = (-5)$, $8 + (-3) = 5$

Subtracting: $(-6) - (-4) = -6 + 4 = -2$, $(-2) - (-7) = -2 + 7 = 5$

Multiplying and Dividing: numbers with like signs give a positive answer; numbers with unlike signs give a negative answer.

$3 \times (-7) = -21$, $(-3) \times (-7) = 21$, $(-3) \times 7 = -21$
$20 \div (-4) = -5$, $(-20) \div 4 = -5$, $(-20) \div (-4) = 5$

Substitution

If $x = -5, y = -3$ and $z = 4$, then

$xy = (-5) \times (-3) = 15$, $x + y = (-5) + (-3) = -8$
$xz = (-5) \times 4 = -20$, $x - y = (-5) - (-3) = -5 + 3 = -2$
$(2x)^2 = (-10)^2 = 100$ but $2x^2 = 2 \times (-5)^2 = 2 \times 25 = 50$

Exercise 19

State the values of:

1. $(-10) + 4$ 2. $10 - 4$ 3. $(-10) - 4$ 4. $10 - (-4)$
5. $(-10) + (-4)$ 6. $(-10) - (-4)$ 7. $5 \times (-8)$ 8. $(-5) \times 8$
9. $(-10) \times (-8)$ 10. $(-6)^2$ 11. $(-3)^3$ 12. $12 - 3$
13. $12 - (-3)$ 14. $(-12) - 3$ 15. $(-12) - (-3)$ 16. $1 - (-1)$

If $a = -3, b = 6, c = -1$ and $d = 0$, find the value of:

17. $a + b$ 18. ab 19. $a - b$ 20. $b \div a$
21. $a - c$ 22. ac 23. bd 24. $b \div c$

25. $2a^2$ 26. $(2a)^2$ 27. $3c$ 28. $b - 3c$

29. $(a + b)^2$ 30. $(a + c)^2$ 31. $(bd + c)^2$ 32. $7c^2$

If $e = \frac{1}{3}, f = 6$ and $g = -2$, find the value of:

33. fg 34. fe 35. $f - g$ 36. $f^2 - g^2$

37. $(f - g)^2$ 38. $f \div g$ 39. $f^2 \div g^2$ 40. $ef + g$

41. g^3 42. $e^2 f$ 43. $(5g)^2$ 44. $5g^2$

45. State the value of x^2 for $x = 3, 1, 0, -1, -3$

46. State the value of $-x^2$ for $x = 3, 1, 0, -1, -3$

47. State the value of u^3 for $u = 2, 1, 0, -1, -2$

48. State the value of $6/x$ for $x = 6, 5, 3, -3, -5$

49. Find the value of $3w + 4$ for $w = 2, 0, -2, -4$

50. Find the value of $6 - 4n$ for $n = 1, 2, -1, -2$

51. Find the value of $3k^2$ for $k = 2, 1, 0, -1, -2$

52. Find the value of $12 - u^3$ for $u = 3, 2, -2, -3$

53. Find the value of $x^2 - 3x$ for $x = 2, 1, 0, -1, -2$

54. Find the value of $6/(u - 2)$ for $u = 5, 4, 3, 1, 0, -1$

55. If $y = x^2 - 5x - 3$ find the value of y when $x = 3, 2, -2, -3$

56. If $y = 7 - 2x - x^2$ find the value of y when $x = 3, 2, -2, -3$

57. If $f(x) = x^3 + 5x$, calculate the value of $f(2)$. This means put $x = 2$ in $x^3 + 5x$. Also calculate the value of $f(-2)$ and $f(-3)$.

58. If $g(x) = x^3 - 4x^2 + 5x - 6$, calculate the value of $g(3)$ and $g(-1)$.

59. If $h(n) = 10 + 3n - 3n^2 - n^3$, calculate the value of $h(1)$, $h(2)$, $h(-1)$ and $h(-2)$.

Simplification

$5a + 7b + 6a - 3b = 5a + 6a + 7b - 3b = 11a + 4b$

$4d \times 3d = 4 \times d \times 3 \times d = 4 \times 3 \times d \times d = 12d^2$

$5e^2 f \times 2ef^3 = 5 \times e^2 \times f \times 2 \times e \times f^3 = (5 \times 2) \times (e^2 \times e) \times (f \times f^3)$
$$= 10e^3 f^4$$

$$\frac{3np^2}{6n^2 p} = \frac{3 \times n \times p \times p}{6 \times n \times n \times p} = \frac{3p}{6n} = \frac{p}{2n}$$

Exercise 20

Simplify:

1. $3a + 7a + 5a$ 2. $8b - 3b + 2b$ 3. $2c + 4d + c + 2d$

4. $7e + 9f - 3e - 4f$ 3. $g \times g \times g \times h \times h$ 6. $3k \times 5m$

7. $6n \times 2n$ 8. $p^5 \times p^4$ 9. $4r^3 \times 3r$
10. $5t \times 2t \times 3t$ 11. $(u^3)^4$ 12. $(5v^5)^2$
13. $w^8 \div w^2$ 14. $24x^2 \div 4x^2$ 15. $30y^3 \div 10y$
16. $10n^4 p^4 \div 2n^3 p$ 17. $(-5a) \times (-2a)$ 18. $(-3b) \times (-b) \times (-2c)$
19. $(-12d^3) \div (3d)$ 20. $(-18f^6) \div (-6f^3)$ 21. $g^7 \times g \div g^8$

Brackets

Each term inside the brackets is multiplied by the term outside the brackets.

$5(a - 3) = 5a - 15; \quad 2b(5b + 3c) = 10b^2 + 6bc; \quad (e - f)f = ef - f^2$
$-d^3(4 - d^4) = -4d^3 + d^7; \quad -3f(f - 2g + h) = -3f^2 + 6fg - 3fh$

Exercise 21

Simplify:

1. $3(a + 4)$ 2. $4(b - 3)$ 3. $c(c + 5)$ 4. $(d - 2)d$
5. $(7 - e)e$ 6. $5f(3f + 2)$ 7. $4g(2h + k)$ 8. $m^3(m + p)$
9. $(n^2 + p^2)p$ 10. $-3q(2 - q)$ 11. $\frac{1}{3}(6r + 9)$
12. $n(a + b - c)$ 13. $2x(x + 3y + z)$ 14. $-t(r - 3t - 2x)$
15. $2(a + 1) + 3(a + 2)$ 16. $5(b - 2) + 2(b + 5)$ 17. $3(c - 5) - 2(c + 4)$
18. $d(d + 2) - 3d(2 - d)$19. $g(3h + k) - h(k + 2g)$ 20. $m(2 - 3m) - (m + 5)$

Binomial products

$(a + b)u = au + bu$. Putting $u = (c + d)$ we have

$(a + b)(c + d) = a(c + d) + b(c + d) = ac + ad + bc + bd$

Similarly, $(n + 5)(p + 3) = n(p + 3) + 5(p + 3) = np + 3n + 5p + 15$
$\quad\quad\quad\quad (x + 7)(x - 2) = x(x - 2) + 7(x - 2) = x^2 - 2x + 7x - 14$
$\quad\quad\quad\quad\quad\quad\quad\quad\quad\quad\quad\quad\quad\quad\quad\quad\quad = x^2 + 5x - 14$
$(y - 4)(y - 5) = y(y - 5) - 4(y - 5) = y^2 - 5y - 4y + 20 = y^2 - 9y + 20$
$(2g - 5)(3h + 4) = 2g(3h + 4) - 5(3h + 4) = 6gh + 8g - 15h - 20$

Exercise 22

Simplify:

1. $(f + 2)(g + 3)$ 2. $(h + 4)(h + 5)$ 3. $(m - p)(m + t)$
4. $(k + 5)(n - 2)$ 5. $(r - 7)(r - 1)$ 6. $(8 - u)(7 + u)$
7. $(2a + 1)(3b + 1)$ 8. $(3c + 4)(c + 5)$ 9. $(2d - 5)(3d + 1)$
10. $(6 - h)(5 - 3h)$ 11. $(7 + 4m)(2 - 3m)$ 12. $(p + 2q)(3p - q)$
13. $(u - 2x)(2u - x)$ 14. $(w + 7)(w - 7)$ 15. $(8 - x)(8 + x)$
16. $(3y + 4)(3y - 4)$ 17. $(3a + 5)^2$ 18. $(2b - 7)^2$
19. $(x + 3)(x^2 - x - 5)$ 20. $(y - 2)(y^2 + 2y - 7)$

Three Important Identities

$(A + B)^2 = A^2 + 2AB + B^2$ $[(A + B)(A + B) = A^2 + AB + BA + B^2]$
$(A - B)^2 = A^2 - 2AB + B^2$ $[(A - B)(A - B) = A^2 - AB - BA + B^2]$
$(A + B)(A - B) = A^2 - B^2$ $[(A + B)(A - B) = A^2 - AB + BA - B^2]$
Putting $A = 5n$ and $B = 3p$, $(5n + 3p)(5n - 3p) = (5n)^2 - (3p)^2$
$$= 25n^2 - 9p^2$$

Exercise 23

Use the above identities to simplify:

1. $(a + 3)^2$ 2. $(b + 5)^2$ 3. $(c + 1)^2$ 4. $(4 + d)^2$
5. $(e - 3)^3$ 6. $(f - 2)^2$ 7. $(7 - g)^2$ 8. $(1 - h)^2$
9. $(3k + 4)^2$ 10. $(2n - 5)^2$ 11. $(p - \frac{1}{2})^2$ 12. $(q + \frac{1}{3})^2$
13. $(r + \frac{2}{3})^2$ 14. $(t - \frac{3}{5})^2$ 15. $(3y + 2x)^2$ 16. $(5n - 3k)^2$
17. $(a + 5)(a - 5)$ 18. $(8 - b)(8 + b)$ 19. $(3c + 2)(3c - 2)$
20. $(5d - 1)(5d + 1)$ 21. $(3e + 4f)(3e - 4f)$ 22. $(2 - h^2)(2 + h^2)$
23. $(3n + \frac{1}{3})(3n - \frac{1}{3})$

Factors

Examples:
$3x + 3y = 3(x + y)$; $na - nb = n(a - b)$;
$m^3 + m^5 = m^3(1 + m^2)$; $10gh - 15g^2 = 5g(2h - 3g)$
$379 \times 268 - 379 \times 258 = 379(268 - 258) = 379(10) = 3790$

Exercise 24

Factorise:

1. $5a + 5b$ 2. $7c - 7d$ 3. $fg + fh$ 4. $kn - 3k$
5. $2p + 6$ 6. $3r - 15$ 7. $t^2 - 7t$ 8. $w^2 + wx$
9. $y^2 - y$ 10. $a^5 + a^2$ 11. $b + b^3$ 12. $3c^2 - 6c$
13. $10df + 15dg$ 14. $21h^2 - 14hn$ 15. $px^2 + p^2x$ 16. $y^4z^3 - y^3z^4$
17. $3a + 6b + 9c$ 18. $d^2 - de + 2d$ 19. $6fg - 4g^2 - 2gh$
20. Factorise $x^2 - xy$. Use the result to find the value of
    $87^2 - 87 \times 77$ and $9.5^2 - 9.5 \times 7.5$
21. By factorising, find the value of $234 \times 53 + 234 \times 32 + 234 \times 15$

Use of $A^2 - B^2 = (A + B)(A - B)$
Examples:
$x^2 - 25 = x^2 - 5^2 = (x + 5)(x - 5)$
$9y^2 - 1 = (3y)^2 - 1^2 = (3y + 1)(3y - 1)$

26

$2n^2 - 8 = 2(n^2 - 4) = 2(n + 2)(n - 2)$
$7.9^2 - 5.9^2 = (7.9 + 5.9)(7.9 - 5.9) = 13.8 \times 2 = 27.6$

Exercise 25

Factorise:
1. $a^2 - 16$ 2. $b^2 - 49$ 3. $81 - c^2$ 4. $1 - 25d^2$
5. $e^2 f^2 - 1$ 6. $4 - g^8$ 7. $9k^2 - 25$ 8. $16 - 81m^2$
9. $2p^2 - 18$ 10. $h^3 - 9h$ 11. $75 - 3t^2$ 12. $9u^2 - 81$
Use factors to find the value of:
13. $102^2 - 98^2$ 14. $65^2 - 35^2$ 15. $10.8^2 - 9.2^2$ 16. $7.7^2 - 6.7^2$

Quadratic expressions
$(x + 9)(x + 4) = x^2 + 4x + 9x + 9 \times 4 = x^2 + (4 + 9)x + 9 \times 4 = x^2 + 13x + 36$
Similarly $(y + 7)(y + 11) = y^2 + (7 + 11)y + 7 \times 11 = y^2 + 18y + 77$
$(n - 6)(n + 2) = n^2 + (-6 + 2)n + (-6)2 = n^2 - 4n - 12$
$(c - 5)(c - 8) = c^2 + (-5 - 8)c + (-5)(-8) = c^2 - 13c + 40$
To factorise $x^2 + 7x + 10$ we seek two numbers having a sum of 7 and a
product of 10. They are 2 and 5 and so $x^2 + 7x + 10 = (x + 2)(x + 5)$
For $y^2 - y - 6$ we seek two numbers having a sum of -1 and a product of
-6. They are -3 and $+2$ and so $y^2 - y - 6 = (y - 3)(y + 2)$

Exercise 26

1. Use the above method to expand:
   (a) $(a + 2)(a + 5)$ (b) $(b + 4)(b + 1)$ (c) $(c + 8)(c + 3)$
   (d) $(d - 2)(d - 3)$ (e) $(e - 5)(e - 7)$ (f) $(f - 1)(f - 9)$
   Factorise:
2. $a^2 + 6a + 5$ 3. $b^2 + 8b + 7$ 4. $c^2 + 2c + 1$ 5. $d^2 - 3d + 2$
6. $e^2 - 4e + 3$ 7. $f^2 - 12f + 11$ 8. $a^2 + 10a + 21$ 9. $b^2 + 14b + 24$
10. $c^2 + 10c + 24$ 11. $d^2 - 7d + 6$ 12. $e^2 - 10e + 16$ 13. $f^2 - 8f + 16$
14. Use the above method to expand:
    (a) $(g - 4)(g + 7)$ (b) $(h - 5)(h + 3)$ (c) $(k + 7)(k - 10)$
    Factorise:
15. $a^2 + 3a - 10$ 16. $b^2 - 3b - 10$ 17. $c^2 - 9c - 10$
18. $d^2 + 2d - 15$ 19. $e^2 - 14e - 15$ 20. $f^2 + 2f - 8$
21. Expand $(2x + 3)(x + 1)$ and $(2x + 1)(x + 3)$. Hence factorise $2x^2 + 5x + 3$.
22. Expand $(3y - 5)(y - 2)$, $(3y - 2)(y - 5)$, $(3y - 1)(y - 10)$ and
    $(3y - 10)(y - 1)$.
    Hence state the factors of (a) $3y^2 - 11y + 10$ (b) $3y^2 - 17y + 10$
23. Expand $(3n - 2)(n + 1)$, $(3n + 2)(n - 1)$, $(3n - 1)(n + 2)$ and
    $(3n + 1)(n - 2)$.
    State the factors of (a) $3n^2 + 5n - 2$ (b) $3n^2 + n - 2$

Factorise:

24. $2a^2 + 3a + 1$
25. $2b^2 + 7b + 5$
26. $2c^2 - 3c + 1$
27. $2d^2 - 9d + 7$
28. $2e^2 - 11e + 5$
29. $3f^2 - 8f + 5$
30. $2g^2 + 3g - 5$
31. $2h^2 + 9h - 5$
32. $3k^2 - 2k - 5$
33. $3m^2 - 14m - 5$
34. $3n^2 + 4n - 7$
35. $2p^2 - 13p - 7$
36. $3 - 4a + a^2$
37. $15 + 14b - b^2$
38. $1 - 5c - 6c^2$
39. $d^3 + 5d^2 + 6d$
40. $f^3 - f^2 - 6f$
41. $3g^2 - 9g + 6$

Four term expressions
Example

$xy + 5x + 3y + 15$
$= (xy + 5x) + (3y + 15)$
$= x(y + 5) + 3(y + 5)$
$= xb + 3b$ where b replaces $(y + 5)$
$= (x + 3)b = (x + 3)(y + 5)$

Example

$6 + 2np - 3n - 4p$
$= 6 - 3n - 4p + 2np$
$= (6 - 3n) - (4p - 2np)$
$= 3(2 - n) - 2p(2 - n)$
$= 3b - 2pb$ where $b = (2 - n)$
$= (3 - 2p)b = (3 - 2p)(2 - n)$

Exercise 27

Factorise:

1. $a(b + 3) + 5(b + 3)$
2. $c(d + e) - f(d + e)$
3. $gh + 4h + 3g + 12$
4. $kn - kp + mn - mp$
5. $r^2 + ru - 3u - 3r$
6. $xy - 5x - y^2 + 5y$
7. $ab - 7a + 3b - 21$
8. $cd - 4c + d - 4$
9. $f + g + fh + gh$
10. $kp + 3ku + 2mp + 6mu$
11. $ab + 12 + 4a + 3b$
12. $c^2 - 5x + 5c - cx$

The factor theorem
If f(x) is given and f(a) = 0, then $(x - a)$ is a factor of f(x).
Example: Let f(x) = $x^3 - 4x^2 - x + 12$.
f(3) = $27 - 36 - 3 + 12 = 0$ and so $(x - 3)$ is a factor of f(x)
Let $x^3 - 4x^2 - x + 12 = (x - 3)(x^2 + ax + b)$
On expansion, $(-3) \times b = 12$ and so $b = -4$
Also $ax^2 - 3x^2 = -4x^2, a - 3 = -4, a = -1$
Thus $x^3 - 4x^2 - x + 12 = (x - 3)(x^2 - x - 4)$

Exercise 28

1. f(x) = $2x^2 + x - 21$. Find f(1), f(2), f(3) and f(4). Hence factorise f(x).
2. g(x) = $5x^2 + x - 4$. Find g(1), g(2), g(−1) and g(−2). Hence factorise g(x).
3. h(x) = $x^3 + x^2 - 7x + 2$. Find h(1), h(−1) and h(2). Hence factorise h(x).

4. $f(u) = u^3 + 4u + 5$. Find $f(1)$, $f(-1)$ and $f(2)$ and so factorise $f(u)$.
5. $g(v) = v^3 - 2v^2 - 5v + 6$. Find $g(1)$, $g(2)$, $g(3)$, $g(-1)$, $g(-2)$ and $g(-3)$. Hence state the factors of $g(v)$.

Use the factor theorem to factorise:

6. $3x^2 - 10x + 8$ 7. $5x^2 - 4x - 12$ 8. $x^3 - 2x^2 - 2x + 1$
9. $x^3 - 2x^2 - x + 2$ 10. $n^3 + 2n^2 - 5n - 6$
11. Find the value of n so that $x - 2$ is a factor of $3x^2 - 2x - n$. Also find the other factor.
12. Find the value of q so that $x + 5$ is a factor of $2x^2 + qx - 15$.
13. Find the value of k so that $x - 2$ is a factor of $x^3 - 3x^2 + 5x + k$.
14. Find the value of p so that $u + 3$ is a factor of $u^3 + 2u^2 + pu - 12$.
15. Find b and c so that both $x - 1$ and $x + 2$ are factors of $x^3 + bx^2 + cx + 6$. What is the other factor?

Algebraic fractions

Questions on fractions involving letters are worked in the same way as those involving numbers only. (See page 2)

$\dfrac{a}{b}, \dfrac{3a}{3b}, \dfrac{ac}{bc}, \dfrac{a(h+k)}{b(h+k)}, \dfrac{a^2}{ab}$ are equivalent fractions.

Reduction of fractions to their lowest terms

$$\frac{5de}{10df} = \frac{5 \times d \times e}{2 \times 5 \times d \times f} = \frac{e}{2f}; \quad \frac{-8n^2x}{-6nx^2} = \frac{4n}{3x}$$

Addition and subtraction

$$x + \frac{u}{y} = \frac{xy}{y} + \frac{u}{y} = \frac{xy + u}{y};$$

$$\frac{a}{n} + \frac{b}{p} = \frac{ap}{np} + \frac{bn}{np} = \frac{ap + bn}{np}; \quad \frac{2}{3c} - \frac{5}{6d} = \frac{4d}{6cd} - \frac{5c}{6cd} = \frac{4d - 5c}{6cd}$$

Expressing a single fraction as two fractions added together

$$\frac{3a^2 + 2b^2}{ab} = \frac{3a^2}{ab} + \frac{2b^2}{ab} = \frac{3a}{b} + \frac{2b}{a}$$

$$\frac{e}{f} \times \frac{fg}{e^2} = \frac{efg}{fe^2} = \frac{g}{e}; \quad \frac{h}{3k} \div \frac{h^2}{6kn} = \frac{h}{3k} \times \frac{6kn}{h^2} = \frac{6hkn}{3h^2k} = \frac{2n}{h}$$

Exercise 29

Copy and complete:

1. $\dfrac{c}{d} = \dfrac{}{5d} = \dfrac{}{df} = \dfrac{}{d^2}$

2. $\dfrac{m}{p} = \dfrac{}{pr} = \dfrac{}{3p} = \dfrac{mt}{}$

3. $\dfrac{3}{u} = \dfrac{6}{} = \dfrac{}{ux} = \dfrac{}{5uy}$

4. $\dfrac{k}{4} = \dfrac{3k}{} = \dfrac{kn}{} = \dfrac{}{16k}$

5. $\dfrac{5}{2} = \dfrac{}{3} = \dfrac{}{} = \dfrac{35}{}$

6. $x = \dfrac{}{5} = \dfrac{}{y} = \dfrac{3x}{}$

7. $\dfrac{f}{g} = \dfrac{}{g(h+2)} = \dfrac{f(n-3)}{}$

8. $\dfrac{5}{m} = \dfrac{}{m(m-1)} = \dfrac{}{m^2+9m} = \dfrac{5m+5t}{}$

Reduce to their lowest terms:

9. $\dfrac{gh}{gk}; \dfrac{3n}{8n}; \dfrac{5r}{ru}$

10. $\dfrac{3}{3x}; \dfrac{a}{ab}; \dfrac{c}{c^2}$

11. $\dfrac{5ef}{5fg}; \dfrac{2p^2}{8pq}; \dfrac{6x^2}{3x}$

12. $\dfrac{a}{a^3}; \dfrac{b^4}{b}; \dfrac{2c^3}{c^5}$

13. $\dfrac{d(e+f)}{g(e+f)}; \dfrac{4g+4h}{5g+5h}$

14. $\dfrac{6(k-m)}{4(k-m)}; \dfrac{5n-10}{3n-6}$

Simplify, giving each as a single fraction:

15. $\dfrac{a}{3} + \dfrac{b}{5}$

16. $\dfrac{c}{2} - \dfrac{d}{7}$

17. $\dfrac{3}{e} + \dfrac{2}{f}$

18. $\dfrac{1}{h} - \dfrac{2}{m}$

19. $\dfrac{k}{4} + \dfrac{k}{3}$

20. $\dfrac{1}{2n} + \dfrac{1}{3n}$

21. $\dfrac{3}{2p} - \dfrac{2}{3p}$

22. $\dfrac{5}{u} + \dfrac{1}{u^2}$

23. $\dfrac{2}{x^2} - \dfrac{4}{x}$

24. $\dfrac{1}{np} - \dfrac{1}{nq}$

25. $\dfrac{c}{2d^2} - \dfrac{5}{3d}$

26. $\dfrac{5}{6ef} + \dfrac{2}{9f^2}$

27. $g - \dfrac{h}{m}$

28. $3 + \dfrac{k}{n}$

29. $\dfrac{5}{p} + r$

30. $\dfrac{2}{x} - x$

Express as two fractions added together:

31. $\dfrac{3a+5b}{15}$

32. $\dfrac{cx+dy}{cd}$

33. $\dfrac{4+f}{f^2}$

34. $\dfrac{g+h}{g^2}$

Express as a single fraction:

35. $\dfrac{3}{x+1} + \dfrac{4}{x-1}$

36. $\dfrac{1}{y-2} + \dfrac{2}{y+2}$

37. $\dfrac{5}{a+3} - \dfrac{4}{a+2}$

38. $\dfrac{1}{b+5} - \dfrac{5}{b+1}$ **39.** $\dfrac{1}{x-3} - \dfrac{1}{x+3}$ **40.** $\dfrac{3}{4-d} - \dfrac{5}{4+d}$

Simplify, giving each answer as a single fraction:

41. $\dfrac{a}{b} \times \dfrac{a}{c}$ **42.** $\dfrac{d}{e} \times \dfrac{f}{e}$ **43.** $\dfrac{2}{g} \times \dfrac{h}{3}$ **44.** $\dfrac{k}{6} \times \dfrac{3}{m}$

45. $\dfrac{n}{p} \times \dfrac{t}{n}$ **46.** $\dfrac{u}{6} \times \dfrac{4}{u}$ **47.** $\dfrac{w}{3} \times \dfrac{3}{w^2}$ **48.** $\dfrac{x^2}{5} \times \dfrac{10}{x}$

49. $\dfrac{3y}{z} \times \dfrac{z}{6y}$ **50.** $\dfrac{4n^2}{pr} \times \dfrac{r}{8n}$ **51.** $\dfrac{a}{b} \div \dfrac{c}{d}$ **52.** $\dfrac{e}{3} \div \dfrac{f}{4}$

53. $\dfrac{g}{2} \div \dfrac{5}{h}$ **54.** $\dfrac{k}{3} \div \dfrac{1}{k}$ **55.** $\dfrac{1}{p} \div \dfrac{p}{3}$ **56.** $\dfrac{r}{2} \div \dfrac{r}{5}$

57. $\dfrac{t}{u} \div \dfrac{3t}{5x}$ **58.** $\dfrac{h^2 n}{5} \div \dfrac{hn^2}{10}$

59. $\dfrac{(a+b)}{7} \times \dfrac{5}{(a+b)}$ **60.** $\dfrac{c}{(e-f)} \times \dfrac{(e-f)}{g}$ **61.** $\dfrac{(n+3)}{5} \div \dfrac{(n+3)}{2}$

62. $\dfrac{7}{x-4} \div \dfrac{5}{x-4}$ **63.** $\dfrac{1}{y-z} \div \dfrac{x}{y-z}$

Simplify:

64. $\dfrac{2a-2b}{6}$ **65.** $\dfrac{3c+3d}{c+d}$ **66.** $\dfrac{ef-f^2}{5e-5f}$ **67.** $\dfrac{k^2-3k}{5k}$

68. $\dfrac{n^2-x^2}{n+x}$ **69.** $\dfrac{m^2-4}{m^2-5m+6}$ **70.** $\dfrac{y^2+6y+5}{y^2-25}$

Linear equations

Examples:

$$3x + 8 = 15$$
$$3x + 8 - 8 = 15 - 8$$
$$3x = 7$$
$$x = \tfrac{7}{3} = 2\tfrac{1}{3}$$

$$9x - 4(x - 5) = 2(x + 7)$$
$$9x - 4x + 20 = 2x + 14$$
$$5x + 20 = 2x + 14$$
$$3x + 20 = 14$$
$$3x = -6$$
$$x = -2$$

$$\frac{x}{4} + \frac{x}{3} = 14$$

Multiplying each side by 12,

$$\frac{12x}{4} + \frac{12x}{3} = 168$$
$$3x + 4x = 168$$
$$7x = 168$$
$$x = 24$$

$$\frac{x+4}{6} - \frac{2x+5}{3} = \frac{1}{2}$$

Multiplying each term by 6,

$$\frac{6(x+4)}{6} - \frac{6(2x+5)}{3} = \frac{6}{2}$$
$$(x+4) - 2(2x+5) = 3$$
$$x + 4 - 4x - 10 = 3$$
$$-3x - 6 = 3$$
$$-3x = 9$$
$$x = \frac{9}{-3} = -3$$

Exercise 30

Solve the following equations:

1. $x + 3 = 7$ 2. $y - 3 = 7$ 3. $3n = 15$ 4. $\frac{1}{2}p = 4$

5. $\frac{x}{3} = 5$ 6. $2y = 7$ 7. $2n + 5 = 11$ 8. $3y - 2 = 10$

9. $2x + 7 = 1$ 10. $5x + 1 = -9$ 11. $3p - 4 = 1$ 12. $\frac{1}{3}y + 8 = 5$

13. $4 + 7n = 3n + 16$ 14. $20 - 8x = 3x + 9$ 15. $2y - 7 = 8 - 3y$

16. $2(p - 4) = 3(p - 2)$ 17. $3(7 - r) = 5(5 - r)$

18. $3(x - 5) - 2(x - 6) = 3$ 19. $2(3y - 4) - (3y + 1) = y$

20. $(n + 4)(n - 2) = n^2$ 21. $3t(t + 2) - t(3t - 1) = 14$

22. $(2 - p)(3 - p) = (1 + p)(4 + p)$

23. $(y - 3)^2 + 5 = (y - 5)(y - 2)$

24. $\frac{x}{2} + \frac{x}{3} = 10$ 25. $\frac{y}{2} - \frac{y}{3} = \frac{5}{6}$ 26. $\frac{n}{5} - \frac{n}{2} = \frac{1}{2}$ 27. $\frac{9x}{10} - \frac{2x}{5} = 3$

28. $0.6p - 0.7 = 1.1$ (*Multiply each term by 10*)

29. $1.3x = 0.8x + 2.4$ 30. $4y - 1.8 = 2.5y$

31. $\frac{n}{2} - \frac{n+5}{4} = 3$ 32. $\frac{h+2}{5} + \frac{h+4}{3} = 2$

33. $\frac{4x-1}{3} - \frac{2x+1}{2} = 1$ 34. $\frac{y+1}{5} = 1 + \frac{y-3}{7}$

35. I write down a certain number, multiply it by 3 and then add on 5. The answer is 23. Let the number be x. Write down an equation for x and solve it.

36. Mr Smith is three times as old as his son Tom. The sum of their ages is 56 years. Taking Tom's age as n years, write down an equation for n and solve it.

37. The perimeter of a rectangle is 38 cm. The length is 3 cm greater than the width. Taking the width as w cm, form an equation for w and solve it.

38. Find three consecutive odd numbers such that their sum is 75. (Take the smallest number as x. Then the middle number is $x + 2$.)

39. 16 articles are bought for 107p. Some of them cost 8p each and the others cost 5p each. Let x be the number of 8p articles. Form an equation for x and, by solving it, find the number of each kind of article bought.

40. In a game, x counters were shared equally among 5 players. Write down an expression for the number each received. In another game the same x counters were shared equally among 3 players. Each received 8 more counters than each player in the first game. Form an equation for x and solve it.

41. When some cards were dealt to 6 players each received 3 more than when they were dealt to 8 players. Find the number of cards.

42. A boat travelled 26 kilometres in 2 hours. For the first x km the speed was 15 km/h and for the rest of the journey it was 12 km/h. Form an equation for x and solve it.

Quadratic equations

$ax^2 + bx + c = 0$, where a, b and c are constants.

Equations with rational roots. Solution by factorisation.
Examples:

$x^2 + 5x = 0$

$x(x + 5) = 0$

$x = 0$ or $(x + 5) = 0$

$x = 0$ or -5

$6x^2 + 13x = 5$

$6x^2 + 13x - 5 = 0$

$(3x - 1)(2x + 5) = 0$

$(3x - 1) = 0$ or $(2x + 5) = 0$

$3x = 1$ or $2x = -5$

$x = \frac{1}{3}$ or $-2\frac{1}{2}$

Exercise 31

Solve the equations:

1. $x^2 - 8x + 15 = 0$
2. $x^2 - 6x + 8 = 0$
3. $x^2 + 7x + 12 = 0$
4. $x^2 - 5x - 14 = 0$
5. $x^2 + 3x - 18 = 0$
6. $x^2 - 7x - 8 = 0$
7. $x^2 - 3x = 0$
8. $x^2 - 25 = 0$
9. $x^2 + 4x = 0$
10. $x^2 = 36$
11. $x^2 + 2x = 15$
12. $x^2 + 6 = 7x$
13. $2x^2 - 7x + 3 = 0$
14. $3x^2 - 5x + 2 = 0$
15. $3x^2 + x = 2$

33

16. $3x^2 - 4x = 0$ **17.** $4x^2 - 9 = 0$ **18.** $6x^2 = 5x$

Form equations having the following roots:

19. 7 and 4 **20.** -5 and -2 **21.** -3 and 5

22. 0 and -2 **23.** 0 and $\frac{2}{7}$ **24.** $-2\frac{1}{2}$ and 2

Equations with irrational roots. Solution by completing the square.
It has two basic ideas:
(1) Suppose that we are given the expression $x^2 + 14x$. We can make a perfect square by adding 49. $x^2 + 14x + 49 = (x + 7)^2$
Notice that $49 = 7^2 = (\frac{1}{2} \text{ of } 14)^2$
(2) If $(x - 8)^2 = 11$, then $(x - 8) = \sqrt{11}$ or $-\sqrt{11}$
$$= 3.32 \text{ or } -3.32 \text{ to 2 decimal places}$$
and so $x = 3.32 + 8 = 11.32$ or $-3.32 + 8 = 4.68$ to 2 decimal places.
Example:
$$x^2 - 5x + 2 = 0$$
$$x^2 - 5x = -2$$
$$x^2 - 5x + (\tfrac{5}{2})^2 = -2 + (\tfrac{5}{2})^2$$
$$(x - \tfrac{5}{2})^2 = \tfrac{17}{4}$$
$$x - \tfrac{5}{2} = \pm\sqrt{\tfrac{17}{4}} = \pm\frac{\sqrt{17}}{\sqrt{4}} = \pm\frac{4.123}{2} = \pm 2.06 \text{ to 2 d.p.}$$
$$x = 2.5 + 2.06 \text{ or } 2.5 - 2.06$$
$$= 4.56 \text{ or } 0.44 \text{ to 2 d.p.}$$

Exercise 32

1. Expand $(x + 3)^2$, $(x + 10)^2$, $(x - 8)^2$, $(x - \tfrac{1}{3})^2$, $(x + \tfrac{3}{2})^2$

2. Add a suitable constant to each of the given expressions and make a statement of the form; $x^2 - 3x + \tfrac{9}{4} = (x - \tfrac{3}{2})^2$

    (a) $x^2 + 10x$ (b) $x^2 - 8x$ (c) $x^2 + 20x$ (d) $x^2 - 7x$

    (e) $x^2 + x$ (f) $x^2 - \tfrac{2}{3}x$ (g) $x^2 + \tfrac{5}{3}x$ (h) $x^2 - \tfrac{3}{5}x$

Solve the following equations. Give your answer to 2 d.p. where appropriate:

3. $(x + 3)^2 = 25$ **4.** $(x - 2)^2 = 36$ **5.** $(x - 5)^2 = 1$

6. $(x - 4)^2 = 21$ **7.** $(x + 1)^2 = 5$ **8.** $(x - \tfrac{1}{2})^2 = 3$

Rewrite each equation in the form $(x + a)^2 = b$ where a and b are constants and use your result to solve the equation, correct to 2 d.p.

9. $x^2 - 6x + 4 = 0$ **10.** $x^2 + 8x + 11 = 0$ **11.** $x^2 - 2x - 5 = 0$

12. $x^2 - 3x - 2 = 0$ **13.** $x^2 + 5x + 3 = 0$ **14.** $x^2 - 7x + 5 = 0$

15. $2x^2 - 6x + 3 = 0$ (*First divide each term by 2*)

16. $3x^2 + 9x - 5 = 0$ **17.** $2x^2 - 5x - 1 = 0$ **18.** $3x^2 + 7x = 2$

Simultaneous linear equations

Method 1 Substitution

To solve $\begin{cases} y = 3x - 5 & (1) \\ 5x - 2y = 6 & (2) \end{cases}$

Substitute $3x - 5$ for y in (2)

We then have $\quad 5x - 2(3x - 5) = 6$
$$5x - 6x + 10 = 6$$
$$x = 4$$

Substituting in (1) $y = 12 - 5 = 7$

Checking in (2) $5x - 2y = 20 - 14 = 6$

Method 2 Elimination

$$\begin{cases} 4x + 2y = 6 \\ 5x + 3y = 4 \end{cases} \qquad \begin{matrix}(1)\\(2)\end{matrix}$$

Multiplying (1) by 3 $\qquad 12x + 6y = 18$

Multiplying (2) by -2 $\quad -10x - 6y = -8$

Adding $\qquad\qquad\qquad\quad 2x \qquad\;\; = 10$
$$x = 5$$

Substituting in (1) $\qquad 20 + 2y = 6$
$$2y = -14, \quad y = -7$$

Checking in (2) $\qquad\quad 25 - 21 = 4$

Exercise 33

Solve, by substitution:

1. $y = 3x - 5$
   $x + y = 3$

2. $y = 1 - 2x$
   $x + 2y = 5$

3. $y = 3 - x$
   $x - 2y = 9$

4. $y = 2x - 5$
   $y = 7 - x$

5. $y = 4x - 11$
   $y = 2x + 6$

6. $y = \frac{1}{3}x + 5$
   $y = 2x - 5$

Solve, by elimination:

7. $5x + 2y = 23$
   $3x - 2y = 1$

8. $4x - 3y = 14$
   $2x + y = 12$

9. $7x + y = 4$
   $2x - 3y = 11$

10. $2x + 5y = -3$
    $4x + y = 21$

11. $3x + 2y = 4$
    $7x + 3y = 11$

12. $5x - y = 1$
    $3x - 2y = 9$

13. $3x - 4y = 17$
    $4x + 5y = 2$

14. $2x + 5y = 4$
    $x + 7y = 11$

15. $8x - 5y = 7$
    $7x - 3y = 13$

16. I handed a bundle of £5 and £1 notes into a bank. There were 16 notes and their value was £44. Let x be the number of £5 notes and y the number of £1 notes. Write down two equations for x and y and solve them.

17. 5 oranges and 2 lemons cost 45p. 9 oranges and 3 lemons cost 78p. Find the cost of 1 orange and the cost of 1 lemon.

18. A bag contains 32 coins. Some of them are 5p coins and the others are 2p coins. The total value is £1. How many of each kind are there?

Formulae

Construction
Exercise 34

1. The cost of hiring a coach is £12. How much does each pay if the cost is shared by (a) 30 (b) 25 (c) n people?
2. (a) How many minutes are there in (i) 1 hour (ii) 5 hours (iii) n hours?
   (b) In m minutes there are t seconds. Express m in terms of t.
3. (a) A man is now 27 years old. How old will he be (i) in 5 years time (ii) in 9 years time (iii) in x years time?
   (b) A girl is now k years old. In y years she will be m years old. Express m in terms of k and y.
4. (a) An aircraft is travelling at 540 km per hour. How far does it go in (i) 3 hours (ii) 20 minutes (iii) x hours?
   (b) A space craft has a speed of v km per hour. It travels d km in y hours. Express d in terms of v and y.
5. (a) A car is travelling at 12 m/s. How long does it take for (i) 48 m (ii) 120 m (iii) d m?
   (b) Travelling at v m/s, a runner covers d m in t s. Express t in terms of v and d.
6. An isosceles triangle has two angles of $65°$. Calculate the third angle. If the equal angles are each of size $x°$ and the third is $y°$, write down a formula for y in terms of x.
7. A clock gains 5 seconds each hour. How many seconds does it gain in (a) 7 hours (b) 24 hours (c) t hours?
   How many minutes does it gain in (d) 1 day (e) 3 days (f) x days?
8. A French bank gives f francs for each pound. How many francs does it give for (a) £5 (b) £32 (c) £x?
9. A rectangular block is x cm by y cm by z cm. The total surface area is A cm^2. Express A in terms of x, y and z.
10. A rectangle of length k cm and width w cm has a perimeter of p cm. Express p in terms of k and w.
11. A city reservoir contains v litres of water. Each day x litres are used. After n days without rain, p litres remain. Write down a formula for p.

Express each of the following statements by a formula, using the letters given in brackets:
12. The perimeter of a square is four times the length of a side. (p, x)
13. The average speed for a journey is found by dividing the distance by the time taken. (s, d, t)
14. To estimate the time needed to cook a piece of meat, allow 30 minutes for each kilogramme and an extra 20 minutes. (t, m)
15. To find the size of each angle of a regular polygon, divide 360 by the number of sides and subtract the answer from 180. (θ, n)

Explain the following formulae:

16. $c = \pi d$ for a circle   17. $A = 180 - B - C$ for a triangle
18. $a^2 = b^2 + c^2$ for a triangle   19. $A = \frac{1}{2}bh$ for a triangle

Evaluation

Exercise 35

Find the value of:

1. $3a^2$ when $a = 5$ 2. $90 - x - y$ when $x = 25$ and $y = 30$

3. $180 - \dfrac{360}{n}$ when $n = 12$ 4. $\sqrt{b^2 - c^2}$ when $b = 17$ and $c = 15$

5. $\frac{1}{2}n(n + 1)$ when $n = 10$ 6. $(a + b)(a - b)$ when $a = 7.5$ and $b = 5.5$
7. $u + ft$ when $u = 163, f = -10$ and $t = 5.5$

8. $\dfrac{PRT}{100}$ when $P = 475, R = 6$ and $T = 4$

9. πr^2 when $\pi = 3.14$ and $r = 6.7$ (2 sig. fig.)

10. $\dfrac{a(r^n - 1)}{r - 1}$ when $a = 5, r = 3$ and $n = 4$

11. $\dfrac{my^2}{rg}$ when $m = 6.3, v = 2.2, r = 1.7$ and $g = 9.8$ (3 sig. fig.)

12. If $v^2 = u^2 + 2fs$, find v when $u = 7, f = 4$ and $s = 3$ (2 sig. fig.)

13. If $\dfrac{1}{v} = \dfrac{1}{u} + \dfrac{1}{f}$, find v when $f = 30$ and $u = 70$.

14. If $T = 2\pi\sqrt{\dfrac{x}{g}}$, find T when $x = 2.6, g = 10$ and $\pi = 3.14$ (2 sig. fig.)

Manipulation
The steps used in rearranging formulae are the same as those used in solving equations.
Example 1: Make u the subject of $v^2 = u^2 + 2as$
Subtracting $2as$ from each side, $v^2 - 2as = u^2$
Taking the square root of each side, $u = \sqrt{v^2 - 2as}$
Example 2: Make x the subject of $T = 2\pi\sqrt{\dfrac{x}{g}}$

Dividing both sides by 2π, $\dfrac{T}{2\pi} = \sqrt{\dfrac{x}{g}}$

Squaring both sides, $\dfrac{T^2}{4\pi^2} = \dfrac{x}{g}$

Multiplying by g, $\dfrac{T^2 g}{4\pi^2} = x$

37

Exercise 36

There are two equations in each of the following questions. First solve the equation having numbers and then use exactly the same method for the equation having only letters. At each step, state what you are doing, as in the two examples above:

1. $x + 3 = 8$; $x + a = b$

2. $x - 3 = 8$; $x - c = d$

3. $3x = 8$; $ex = f$

4. $\dfrac{x}{3} = 8$; $\dfrac{x}{g} = h$

5. $x^2 = 36$; $x^2 = k$

6. $\sqrt{x} = 5$; $\sqrt{x} = n$

7. $2\sqrt{x} = 3$; $p\sqrt{x} = r$

8. $\dfrac{3}{5}x = 4$; $\dfrac{t}{u}x = w$

9. $\dfrac{x}{7} = \dfrac{5}{2}$; $\dfrac{x}{a} = \dfrac{b}{c}$

10. $\dfrac{11}{x} = \dfrac{2}{3}$; $\dfrac{d}{x} = \dfrac{e}{f}$

11. $3x - 5 = 7$; $gx - h = k$

12. $\sqrt{x + 4} = 6$; $\sqrt{x + m} = p$

13. $x^2 + 16 = 25$; $x^2 + r^2 = t^2$

14. $\sqrt{\dfrac{10}{x}} = 5$; $\sqrt{\dfrac{u}{x}} = w$

Rearrange the following formulae so that the stated letter is the subject

15. $F = ma$; a

16. $V = x^3$; x

17. $A = \pi r^2$; r

18. $A + B + C = 180$; B

19. $v = u + at$; u

20. $v = u + at$; a

21. $d = \sqrt{(13h)}$; h

22. $t = \frac{1}{3}\sqrt{s}$; s

23. $s = \dfrac{d}{t}$; t

24. $s = \frac{1}{2}gt^2$; t

25. $v = \frac{4}{3}\pi r^3$; r

26. $A = \frac{1}{2}(a + b)h$; h

27. $\dfrac{1}{v} = \dfrac{1}{u} + \dfrac{1}{f}$; u

28. $C = \frac{5}{9}(F - 32)$; F

29. A regular pentagon has n sides. Each angle is $\theta°$ where $\theta = 180 - \dfrac{360}{n}$.

   (a) Calculate θ if $n = 20$ (b) Make n the subject of the formula.
   (c) Calculate n if $\theta = 150$.

30. The arch of a bridge has a width of x cm and a height of h cm, where $x = \sqrt{320h}$. (a) Find x if $h = 20$ (b) Rearrange the formula to make h the subject. (c) Calculate h if $x = 48$.

31. A rectangular box of height h cm has a square base of side x cm. The volume is v cm^3. (a) State the formula for v in terms of h and x. (b) Rearrange the formula to make x the subject. (c) Calculate x if $v = 80$ and $h = 5$.

32. For the box of question **31**, the length of a diagonal from a top corner to the opposite bottom corner is y cm where $y = \sqrt{(h^2 + 2x^2)}$. (a) If $x = 8$ and $h = 5$, calculate y to 1 d.p. (b) Make h the subject of the formula. (c) If $x = 9$ and $y = 14$, calculate h to 1 d.p.

Functions

A function associates each element of one set with one and only one element of another set. The first set is called the **domain** and the second is called the **range**.

The function 'Take a number, double it and add on 5' associates each element of D = {−2, −1, 0, 1, 2} with one member of R = {1, 3, 5, 7, 9}. This function is illustrated in three ways in Fig. 1.

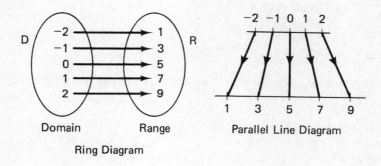

Ring Diagram   Parallel Line Diagram

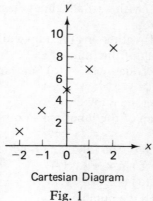

Cartesian Diagram

Fig. 1

Denoting the function by f we can write f: $x \longrightarrow 2x + 5$. 9 is said to be the **image** of 2. We write f(x) for the image of x. Then f(x) = $2x + 5$ and so f(2) = 9.

The calculation for f(x) and f(−2) can be shown thus:

take x $\xrightarrow{\text{double}}$ $2x$ $\xrightarrow{\text{add 5}}$ $2x + 5$

take −2 $\xrightarrow{\text{double}}$ −4 $\xrightarrow{\text{add 5}}$ +1

The operation can be 'undone' as follows (work from right to left);

$$-2 \xleftarrow{\text{halve}} -4 \xleftarrow{\text{subtract 5}} \quad \text{take } +1$$

$$\tfrac{1}{2}(y-5) \xleftarrow{\text{halve}} y-5 \xleftarrow{\text{subtract 5}} \quad \text{take } y$$

By this means each element of R is mapped back to the original element of D. The function which 'undoes' f is called **inverse** of f and is written f^{-1}. Then $f^{-1}: y \longrightarrow \tfrac{1}{2}(y-5)$ and $f^{-1}(9) = 2$.

Suppose that $g: x \rightarrow x^2$ and h: $x \rightarrow x + 3$. hg means 'do g first and then h', and so $5 \xrightarrow{g} 25 \xrightarrow{h} 28$. We write $hg(5) = h(25) = 28$.
Similarly $gh(5) = g(8) = 64$.
hg: $x \rightarrow x^2 + 3$ and gh: $x \rightarrow (x+3)^2$

Exercise 37

1. Find the range of each of the following functions for the given domain D:
   (a) f: $x \rightarrow 3x$ D = $\{-2, -1, 0, 1, 2\}$
   (b) g: $x \rightarrow x + 3$ D = $\{0, 1, 2, 3\}$
   (c) h: $x \rightarrow \tfrac{1}{x}$ D = $\{1, 2, 3, 4\}$
   (d) f: $x \rightarrow x^2$ D = $\{-2, -1, 0, 1, 2, 3\}$
   (e) g: $x \rightarrow 2^x$ D = $\{-2, -1, 0, 1, 2\}$
2. Illustrate question 1 (a) with a parallel lines diagram and a Cartesian diagram.
3. Illustrate question 1 (d) with a ring diagram and a Cartesian diagram.
4. State the inverse of each of the following:
   (a) Subtract 4   (b) Divide by 3   (c) Subtract from 10
   (d) Divide into 30.
   Test your answers using the number 6.
5. State the inverse of each of the functions of question 1 (a), (b) and (c).
6. Find the inverse of each of the following functions:
   (a) f: $x \rightarrow 3x - 1$ (b) g: $x \rightarrow \tfrac{1}{2}x + 4$
   (c) h: $x \rightarrow 15 - 2x$ (d) k: $x \rightarrow \tfrac{30}{x} + 7$
   Test your answers using the number 6.
7. Explain why the function of question 1 (d) has no inverse for the given domain. Restrict the domain so that there is an inverse function and state the inverse function.
8. State the range of each of the following where x is real:
   (a) f: $x \rightarrow 5x$ D = $\{x: 0 \leqslant x \leqslant 1\}$
   (b) g: $x \rightarrow 4 - x$ D = $\{x: 0 \leqslant x \leqslant 4\}$
   (c) h: $x \rightarrow \dfrac{1}{1+x}$ D = $\{x: 0 \leqslant x \leqslant 1\}$
   (d) k: $x \rightarrow 9 - x^2$ D = $\{x: -3 \leqslant x \leqslant 3\}$

40

9. If f: $x \rightarrow 3x$ and g: $x \rightarrow x - 3$, find
   (a) f(5), g(5), fg(5) and gf(5)
   (b) $f^{-1}(6)$, $g^{-1}(6)$, $g^{-1}f^{-1}(6)$ and $f^{-1}g^{-1}(6)$
10. If f: $x \rightarrow x + 3$
   (a) Find f(4), ff(4) and ff(−5)
   (b) State the inverse function and find $f^{-1}(4)$ and $f^{-1}f^{-1}(4)$.
   (c) Express ff(x) in its simplest form.
11. If f: $x \rightarrow 2x - 1$
   (a) Find f(3), f(−3), ff(3) and ff(−3)
   (b) Express ff(x) in its simplest form and check for ff(3) and ff(−3)
   (c) If ff(k) = 5, find k.
12. If f: $x \rightarrow x^2$ and g: $x \rightarrow x + 2$
   (a) Find g(4), fg(4), f(4) and gf(4).
   (b) Express fg(x) and gf(x) in their simplest forms.
   (c) For what value of x is fg(x) = gf(x)?
13. f: $x \rightarrow 2x - 3$ and g: $x \rightarrow x^2 + 3$.
   (a) Show that fg: $x \rightarrow 2x^2 + 3$ and find gf.
   (b) Find fg(−3) and gf(−3).
   (c) Find two values of x for which gf(x) = 4.
14. Two simple functions are such that gf: $x \rightarrow \dfrac{3}{x - 2}$.

   What are f, g and fg? Find gf(1) and fg(1).
15. f: $x \rightarrow x^2 - 3x$. Find (a) the range set whose domain set is $\{2, 0, -2\}$
   (b) the domain set whose range set is $\{4, -2\}$.

Graphs

The gradient of the line joining $(2, 5)$ and $(8, 9)$ is

$$\frac{\text{increase in } y}{\text{increase in } x} = \frac{9 - 5}{8 - 2} = \frac{4}{6} = \frac{2}{3}$$

$y = mx + c$, where m and c are constants, always gives a straight line cutting the x-axis at $(0, c)$ and having a gradient of m. For example, $y = \frac{3}{4}x + 5$ cuts the y-axis at $(0, 5)$ and has a gradient of $\frac{3}{4}$. If this line makes an angle of θ with the direction of the x-axis, then $\tan \theta = \frac{3}{4}$ = 0.75 and so $\theta \doteq 36.9°$.

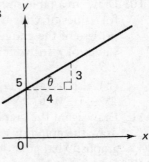

Fig. 2

41

By the gradient of a curve at a point, we mean the gradient of the tangent to the curve at that point.

Exercise 38

1. Using a scale of 2 cm to 1 unit, number an x-axis from -3 to $+3$ and a y-axis from -3 to $+5$. Draw as much as possible of the following graphs, labelling each:
   (a) $y = x$ (b) $y = x + 2$ (c) $y = \frac{3}{2}x$ (d) $y = -x$
   (e) $y = 4 - x$ (f) $y = 3$ (g) $x = -2$

2. For the graph of $y = \frac{2}{3}x + 7$, state (a) where it cuts the y-axis (b) its gradient (c) the angle it makes with the positive direction of the x-axis.

3. State the equation for the straight line which (a) cuts the y-axis at $(0, 6)$ and has a gradient of $\frac{5}{2}$ (b) cuts the y-axis at $(0, -4)$ and has a gradient of $-\frac{4}{3}$.

4. Mark each pair of points and state the gradient of the line joining them: (a) $(0, 0)$ and $(5, 3)$ (b) $(1, 2)$ and $(7, 4)$ (c) $(3, 6)$ and $(8, 2)$ (d) $(-2, 4)$ and $(3, -1)$.

5. Using a scale of 2 cm to 1 unit, number an x-axis from -3 to $+3$ and a y-axis from 0 to 9. Draw the graph of $y = x^2$. From your graph obtain approximate values for 1.7^2, $(-2.2)^2$, $\sqrt{2}$ and $\sqrt{5.8}$.

6. Using the graph drawn in question 5, draw a tangent to the curve $y = x^2$ at $(1.3, 1.69)$ and hence find the gradient of the curve at that point. Repeat for the point $(-2.3, 5.29)$.

7. Using 2 cm to 1 unit number an x-axis from -3 to $+3$ and using 2 cm to 10 units number a y-axis from -30 to $+30$. Draw the graph of $y = x^3$. From your graph find approximate values for 2.2^3, $(-1.8)^3$, $\sqrt[3]{24}$ and $\sqrt[3]{-15}$.

8. Draw up a table showing the values of x and y where $y = \frac{6}{x}$ for $x = -6$, $-4, -3, -2, -1\frac{1}{2}, -1, 1, 2, 3, 4, 6$. Draw the graph of $y = \frac{6}{x}$ using 1 cm to 1 unit on each axis.

9. By drawing tangents to the curve in question 8, find the gradient of $y = \frac{6}{x}$ at $(2, 3)$ and at $(-3, -2)$.

10. Draw up a table showing the values of x and y where $y = x^2 - 2x - 1$ for values of x from -2 to $+4$. Draw the graph of the equation.
    (a) Use of the graph to find (i) the minimum value of y (ii) the range of values of x for which $y < 2$ (iii) the gradient of the graph where $x = 2.5$.
    (b) Also use the graph to find approximations to the roots of (i) $x^2 - 2x - 1 = 0$ (ii) $x^2 - 2x - 5 = 0$.

11. Draw again the graph of $y = x^2$ as in question 5. Using the same axes draw the graph of $y = 3 - x$. State the points of intersection of the graphs. What equation in x is satisfied by the values of x at these points?

12. Draw again the graph of $y = x^3$ as in question 7. Using the same axes draw the graph of $y = 4x + 3$. Show that at the points of intersection of the graphs the values of x satisfy $x^3 - 4x - 3 = 0$ and find these values from your graphs.

Inequalities

If $a > b$, then $a + c > b + c$

If $a > b$, and $c > 0$, then $ac > bc$

If $a > b$ and $c < 0$, then $ac < bc$

If $a > 0$, $b > 0$ and $a > b$, then $\dfrac{1}{a} < \dfrac{1}{b}$

Exercise 39

1. x is an integer. State all possible values of x such that
   (a) $5 < x < 9$ (b) $-6 < x < -3$ (c) $-4 \leqslant x \leqslant 0$
   (d) $5 < 2x \leqslant 12$ (e) $-5 < 3x < 4$ (f) $x^2 < 8$
2. $y \in \{-2, -1, 0, 1, 2, 3, 4\}$. State the possible values of y if
   (a) $y > 2$ (b) $y \leqslant -1$ (c) $y < -2$ (d) $-1 \leqslant y < 1$ (e) $y^2 \leqslant 4$

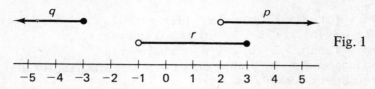

Fig. 1

3. In Fig. 1, line p illustrates $n > 2$ where n is a real number (that is, not just an integer). Line q illustrates $n \leqslant -3$. Line r illustrates $-1 < n \leqslant -3$. When is a hollow ring used and when a solid? What do the arrows on p and q mean?
   Draw figures to illustrate (a) $n > -2$ (b) $n \leqslant 1$ (c) $-3 < n \leqslant 0$
   (d) $2 \leqslant n < 5$
4. If x is a real number, solve the following inequalities:
   (a) $x - 3 > 2$ (b) $x + 5 < -1$ (c) $2x + 3 \geqslant 11$
   (d) $3x - 7 > 5$ (e) $2 + 5x \leqslant 9$ (f) $x - 4 > 7 - 2x$
5. Solve the following where n is a real number and illustrate each as in question 3:
   (a) $3 < n + 4 < 6$ (b) $1 < n - 2 < 3$ (c) $4 < 3 - n < 7$
6. For each of the following statements, say whether it is true or false:
   (a) If $x < 3$ then $5x < 15$ (b) If $x > 4$ then $3x > 7$
   (c) If $x < 2$ then $-x < -2$ (d) If $-x > 3$ then $x < -3$
   (e) If $x - 3 > 0$ then $x < -3$ (f) If $x + 5 > 0$ then $x > -5$
7. State (a) the range of values of x for which $3x + 5 > x + 1$
          (b) the range of values of x for which $x^2 < 25$.
   Show these two ranges on a diagram like Fig 1. Hence express in the form $a < x < b$, the range for which both inequalities are satisfied.
8. Show on a number line the range of values of x which satisfy both $x < 3$ and $x + 3 \leqslant 2x + 5$ simultaneously.
9. If x and y are elements of $\{0, 1, 2, 3, 4\}$, list the members of
   (a) $\{(x, y): y > x\}$ (b) $\{(x, y): y < x - 1\}$
   (c) $\{(x, y): x + y > 6\}$ (d) $\{(x, y): x + y \leqslant 2\}$

10. On squared paper draw the graphs of $x + y = 4$ using axes numbered from -2 to $+6$. This line divides the plane into the three sets of points: $A = \{(x, y): x + y = 4\}$, $B = \{(x, y): x + y > 4\}$ and $C = \{(x, y): x + y < 4\}$.
    (a) Mark the points $(3, 2), (-1, 6), (2, 5), (5, 4)$ with crosses. To which set do they belong? Are they above or below the line?
    (b) Mark the points $(1, 2), (2, 1), (-2, 4), (5, -2)$ with ringed dots. To which set do they belong? Are they above or below the line?

11. Draw the graph of $y = x + 2$ using axes from 0 to 6. Label as P the area containing the points such that $y > x + 2$, and as Q the area containing the points such that $y < x + 2$.

12. Using axes from -5 to $+5$, draw the graph of $y = 3 - \frac{1}{2}x$. Shade the area for which $y < 3 - \frac{1}{2}x$. (Consider some points such as $(2, 1)$.)

   For each part of questions 13–15 make a sketch (using both x and y axes) and shade the part of the plane where the statement is true. Use a broken line if the inequality is $>$ or $<$ and a continuous line if it is $\geqslant$ or $\leqslant$:

13. (a) $x > 3$ (b) $y \leqslant -1$ (c) $y < x$ (d) $x + y \geqslant 3$
14. (a) $1 \leqslant x \leqslant 3$ (b) $-1 < y < 2$ (c) $x \leqslant -1$ and $y > -2$
15. (a) $x + y > 4$ and $y > 2$ (b) $y \leqslant 6 - x$ and $y \leqslant x$
16. On graph paper show by shading the set of points which satisfy all the inequalities $y + x \leqslant 9, y \leqslant 2x, y \geqslant x - 3$ and $y \geqslant 1$.

Fractional indices

$$a^{\frac{1}{q}} = \sqrt[q]{a} \qquad a^{\frac{p}{q}} = \sqrt[q]{(a^p)} \text{ or } (\sqrt[q]{a})^p$$

$$64^{\frac{1}{3}} = \sqrt[3]{64} = 4; \quad \left(\frac{4}{9}\right)^{-\frac{3}{2}} = (\sqrt{\frac{9}{4}})^3 = (\frac{3}{2})^3 = \frac{27}{8}$$

Exercise 40

1. Write in the form a^n:
   (a) $\sqrt[3]{a}$ (b) $\sqrt[5]{a}$ (c) $\frac{1}{a^3}$ (d) $\frac{1}{a^5}$
   (e) $(\sqrt[3]{a})^4$ (f) $\sqrt[5]{(a^2)}$ (g) $\sqrt{(a^7)}$ (h) 1

2. Find the value of:
   (a) $9^{\frac{1}{2}}$ (b) $8^{\frac{1}{3}}$ (c) $16^{\frac{1}{4}}$ (d) 9^0

3. State as fractions without indices:
   (a) 5^{-1} (b) 3^{-2} (c) 2^{-3} (d) $(\frac{3}{5})^{-2}$

44

Find the value of:

4. $4^{\frac{3}{2}}$ 5. $16^{\frac{3}{4}}$ 6. $27^{\frac{2}{3}}$ 7. $8^{\frac{5}{3}}$ 8. $25^{1\frac{1}{2}}$

9. $(\frac{2}{3})^{-2}$ 10. $(\frac{1}{2})^{-3}$ 11. $(\frac{1}{4})^{\frac{1}{2}}$ 12. $(\frac{4}{9})^{1\frac{1}{2}}$ 13. $(\frac{3}{7})^0$

14. $(\frac{9}{16})^{\frac{1}{2}}$ 15. $(64)^{-\frac{1}{3}}$ 16. $16^{-\frac{3}{4}}$ 17. $(\frac{9}{25})^{-\frac{3}{2}}$ 18. $(2\frac{1}{4})^{-\frac{1}{2}}$

Simplify:

19. $k^{\frac{1}{2}} \times k^{\frac{1}{4}}$ 20. $m^{\frac{3}{4}} \div m^{\frac{1}{2}}$ 21. $(n^{\frac{2}{3}})^3$

22. $(p^{\frac{3}{4}})^{\frac{1}{3}}$ 23. $(q^{-\frac{1}{2}})^4$ 24. $(\frac{1}{r})^{-5}$

Variation

$y \propto x$ means 'y is **directly proportional** to x' or 'y **varies directly** as x'. If x is trebled, then y is trebled. There is a formula $y = kx$ where k is a constant. 'y varies directly as the square of x' can be written $y \propto x^2$. If x is trebled, then y is multiplied by 3^2, i.e. 9. There is a formula $y = kx^2$. Suppose that $y = 9$ when $x = 6$. Substituting in $y = kx^2$ we have $9 = 36k$ and so $k = \frac{1}{4}$ and the formula is $y = \frac{1}{4}x^2$.

'y is inversely proportional to x' or 'y varies inversely as x' can be written $y \propto \frac{1}{x}$. If x is doubled, then y is halved. There is a formula $y = \frac{k}{x}$.

Exercise 41

1. Express with the sign α and state the formula using k as above if (a) y varies directly as x^3, (b) A varies directly as the square of r, (c) F is inversely proportional to the square of d.
2. Given that $y = 6$ when $x = 2$, obtain the formula for y in terms of x if
   (a) $y \propto x$ (b) $y \propto \frac{1}{x}$ (c) $y \propto x^3$ (d) $y \propto \frac{1}{x^2}$
3. If $y = 8$ when $x = 5$, find the value of y when $x = 10$ if
   (a) $y \propto x$ (b) $y \propto x^2$ (c) $y \propto \frac{1}{x}$ (d) $y \propto \frac{1}{x^2}$
4. If $y \propto \frac{1}{x}$ and $y = 8$ when $x = 3$, find y when $x = 4$ and find x when $y = 12$.
5. If $m \propto p^3$ and $m = 128$ when $p = 4$, find m when $p = 5$ and find p when $m = 0.25$.
6. A stone takes t seconds to fall h metres, where t varies as the square root of h. If $t = 3$ when $h = 45$, find t when $h = 80$ and find h when $t = 6$.

7. The volume of a given mass of gas is inversely proportional to its pressure. When the pressure is 80 cm of mercury the volume is 150 cm^3. Find (a) the formula for v in terms of p (b) the volume when the pressure is 100 cm of mercury.

8. The following results were obtained in an experiment:

x	3	6	9	12
y	2.1	1.1	0.7	0.5

It is believed that they satisfy the formula $y = k/x$. Plot y against $1/x$ and draw the best straight line through the points. k is the gradient of this line. Find k and state the formula.

9. The following results were obtained in an experiment:

x	0.9	1.4	1.8	2.1	2.3
y	1.1	2.3	3.8	5.4	6.4

Plot y against x^2 and by drawing the best straight line through the points, find the formula for y in terms of x.

Differentiation

To find the gradient of the curve $y = x^3$ at the point (x, y) we **differentiate** the function x^3 and obtain the **derived function**, $3x^2$. At $(2, 8)$ the gradient is $3 \times 2^2 = 12$; at $(-\frac{1}{2}, -\frac{1}{8})$ it is $3 \times (-\frac{1}{2})^2 = \frac{3}{4}$.

The derived function is denoted by $\dfrac{dy}{dx}$.

If $y = x^n$ then $\dfrac{dy}{dx} = n\,x^{n-1}$

If $y = 7x^3 - 5x + 8 - 3x^{-2}$

then $\dfrac{dy}{dx} = 7 \times 3x^2 - 5 - 3(-2)x^{-3} = 21x^2 - 5 + 6x^{-3}$

(Notice that the constant, 8, disappears on differentiation.)

Turning points
For $y = x^3 - 12x + 5$ $\dfrac{dy}{dx} = 3x^2 - 12$

$\dfrac{dy}{dx} = 0$ if $3x^2 - 12 = 0$ that is if $x = \pm 2$

When $x = 2, y = -11$ and when $x = -2, y = 21$

When x is a little less than 2, $\dfrac{dy}{dx} < 0$ and

when x is a little more than 2, $\dfrac{dy}{dx} > 0$.

Thus $(2, -11)$ is a **minimum point**.
Similarly, $(-2, 21)$ is a **maximum point**.
$(2, -11)$ and $(-2, 21)$ are both **turning points**.

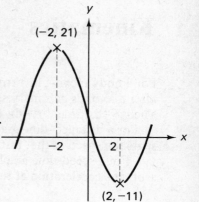

Exercise 42

1. Differentiate x^4, $5x^2$, $8x$, $\dfrac{3}{x}$, $\dfrac{5}{x^2}$

2. Differentiate $x^2 - 3x$, $7 - x^3$, $x - 5x^3$, $\tfrac{1}{2}x^2 + \dfrac{1}{x}$

3. Find $\dfrac{dy}{dx}$ if (a) $y = 2x^2 + 6x$ (b) $y = \dfrac{3}{x} - \dfrac{4}{x^2}$
 (c) $y = 8 + 5x - x^3$

 Find the gradients of the following curves at the given points:

4. $y = x^2$ at $(3, 9)$ 5. $y = \dfrac{6}{x}$ at $(2, 3)$ 6. $y = 2 - x^3$ at $(-1, 3)$

7. $y = x^2 - x$ at $(2, 2)$ 8. $y = 5 - \tfrac{1}{2}x^2$ at $(-2, 3)$ 9. $y = x - \dfrac{4}{x}$ at $(2, -2)$

10. Find the point on $y = x^2 - 6x$ at which the gradient is zero.
11. For the curve $y = 4x - x^2$, find (a) the point at which the tangent is parallel to the x-axis (b) the gradient where $x = 1\tfrac{1}{2}$ and where $x = 2\tfrac{1}{2}$. Is the point of (a) a maximum or a minimum point?
12. Find the maximum value of $8x - x^2$ and the minimum value of $x^2 + 6x + 13$.
13. Find the turning points on the curve $y = x^3 + 3x^2 - 9x$. Sketch the curve.
14. Find the maximum and minimum values of $x^3 - 12x + 3$.
15. Calculate (a) the coordinates of the points where the curve $y = x^2 - 8x + 12$ cuts the axes (b) the value of x for which the gradient is zero (c) the minimum value of y.
16. For the curve $y = x + 9/x$ calculate
 (a) The values of x for which the gradient is zero
 (b) The gradients where $x = -2, -4, 4$ and 2
 (c) The maximum and minimum values of y.
 Sketch the curve.
17. A rectangle has a perimeter of 24 cm. If its length is x cm, express its width in terms of x. Hence express the area, A cm^2, in terms of x. Find the maximum value of A.

Kinematics

For a body moving in a straight line, let the distance, speed and acceleration after t seconds be s metres, v metres per second and f metres per second^2. Then $v = ds/dt$ and $f = dv/dt$.

For a distance–time graph, the gradient of the tangent at a point represents the speed at that instant.

For a speed-time graph, the gradient of the tangent at a point represents the acceleration at that instant.

Exercise 43

1. If $s = 10t - t^2$, find v when $t = 3$.
2. If $v = 3t^2 + 4t$, find f when $t = 1$ and when $t = 3$.
3. If $s = t^3 + 2t^2 + 3$, find v and f when $t = 2$.
4. If $s = 8 + 6t - \frac{1}{2}t^2$, (a) find the initial value of v (i.e. when $t = 0$) (b) find v when $t = 2.5$ (c) find t when $v = 0$.
5. If $s = 3t + 4t^2$, (a) find v when $t = 1.5$ (b) find f. (notice that f is constant.)
6. If $s = t^3 - 12\,t$, find v and f when $t = 3$.
7. A particle starts from rest and moves in a straight line so that the velocity v cm/s, after t s is given by $v = 12t - 3t^2$. Find (a) the velocity after 3 s (b) the time before the particle comes to rest again (c) the acceleration after $\frac{1}{2}$ s (d) the greatest velocity (i.e. when the acceleration is zero).
8. Draw distance–time graphs for the following:
   (a) A boy cycles for 40 min at 15 km/h, stops for 15 min and then continues for 30 min at 10 km/h.
   (b) A boat cruises at 20 km/h for $\frac{3}{4}$ h, stops for $\frac{1}{4}$h and then returns to its starting point in 1 h.
9. A cyclist started from home at 11.30 h to cycle to a friend's house 40 km away. He cycled at a steady speed of 16 km/h but stopped for lunch from 12.45 to 13.15 h. At what time did he arrive? Draw his distance–time graph.
   His parents left home at 13.30 h and travelled along the same road at 60 km/h. Add their distance–time graph. When did they pass him?
10. A stone is dropped from a high cliff. After t s it has fallen s m where $s = 5t^2$. Draw the distance–time graph for the first 6 s. By drawing a tangent to the curve where $t = 3$ and finding its gradient, estimate the speed of the stone after 3 s. Find ds/dt and so calculate the speed of the stone after 3 s.
11. For the boy and the boat in question 1, draw the speed–time graphs.
12. For the cyclist in question 2, draw the speed–time graph.
13. A train accelerated steadily from 0 to 50 km/h in 4 minutes, travelled

48

at that speed for 12 minutes, decelerated to 30 km/h in 4 minutes, stayed at that speed for 5 minutes and then came steadily to rest in 10 minutes. Draw the speed–time graph. When was the train travelling at 20 km/h? State the acceleration and the two decelerations in km/h per min.

14. A body started from A. Its distance from A at various times was:

Time (seconds)	0	10	20	30	40	50	60
Distance (metres)	0	15	65	150	250	285	290

Draw the distance-time graph. By drawing tangents estimate (a) the speed at 20 seconds (b) the greatest speed.

15. The speedometer readings of a car were as follows:

Time from start(s)	0	5	10	15	20	25	30	35	40
Speed (m/s)	0	7	12	15	16	16	17	19	22

Plot points for these values, using 2 cm to 5 s and to 5 m/s and draw a smooth curve through them. Estimate the time at which the speedometer reading was 14 m/s. By drawing tangents, estimate the acceleration at 10 s and at 35 s.

Integration

This is the reverse of differentiation.

Differentiation: If $y = 5x^2 - 4x + 7$ then $\dfrac{dy}{dx} = 10x - 4$

(any other number in place of the 7 would not change the result.)

Integration: If $\dfrac{dy}{dx} = 10x - 4$ then $y = 5x^2 - 4x + c$ where c is any number.

We can write $\int (10x - 4)\, dx = 5x^2 - 4x + c$

In general $\int x^n\, dx = \dfrac{x^{n+1}}{n+1} + c$ provided $n \neq -1$

Exercise 44

Find y if $\dfrac{dy}{dx}$ is:

1. x^2 2. $10x$ 3. $7 - 6x$ 4. $3x^2 - 2x + 5$

Integrate:

5. $3x$ 6. x^3 7. $4x - 3$ 8. $\dfrac{5}{x^2}$

Evaluate:

9. $\int 6x^2 \, dx$ 10. $\int 6x \, dx$ 11. $\int (3x - 9) \, dx$

12. If $\dfrac{dy}{dx} = 2x + 3$ and $y = 3$ when $x = 1$, find y.

13. If $\dfrac{dy}{dx} = 3 - 4x$ and $y = 1$ when $x = 4$, find y.

14. A curve has a gradient of $5 - 2x$ at the point (x, y) and it passes through $(2, 3)$. Find the equation of the curve.

15. A curve has a gradient of $3x^2 - 8x$ at the point (x, y) and it passes through $(1, 2)$. Find the equation of the curve.

For the questions **16** to **19** a particle moving in a straight line is s metres from a fixed point in the line at t seconds, has a velocity of v metres per second and an acceleration of f metres per second per second.

16. If $v = 4t + 3$, find s given that s given that $s = 0$ when $t = 0$.

17. If $v = 3t^2 - 4t$ and $s = 4$ when $t = 1$, find the formula for s.

18. If $f = 2t + 2$ and $v = 4$ when $t = 0$, find the formula for v.

19. If $f = -6$, find the formulae for v and s given that $v = 15$ and $s = 6$ when $t = 2$.

Definite integrals

If $\int f(x) \, dx = F(x)$ then $\int_a^b f(x) \, dx =$
$F(b) - F(a)$. This is the
area bounded by the curve
$y = f(x)$, the lines $x = a$ and
$x = b$ and the x-axis.

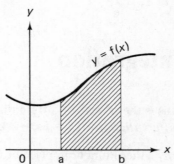

The area between the curve $y = 2x^2$, the x-axis and the lines $x = 3$ and $x = 6$ is $\int_3^6 2x^2 \, dx = |\frac{2}{3}x^3|_3^6 = (\frac{2}{3} \times 216) - (\frac{2}{3} \times 36) = 144 - 24 = 120$

Exercise 45

Evaluate:

1. $\int_1^2 6x \, dx$ 2. $\int_2^3 (2x + 3) \, dx$ 3. $\int_0^2 (6x^2 - 2) \, dx$
4. $\int_{-1}^1 3x^2 \, dx$ 5. $\int_{-2}^4 (8 - x) \, dx$

Find the area bounded by the given curve, the x-axis and the given straight lines:

6. $y = 3x^2$; $x = 2, x = 3$ 7. $y = 9 - x^2$; $x = 0, x = 3$
8. $y = 15 - 3x^2$; $x = 1, x = 2$ 9. $y = 12/x^2$; $x = 2, x = 4$

50

10. Make a sketch to show the area represented by $\int_1^3 (x+1)\,dx$. Calculate the area (a) by dividing it into a rectangle and a triangle (b) by evaluating the integral.

11. Where does the curve $y = 3x(4-x)$ cut the x-axis? By integrating $12x - 3x^2$, find the area between the curve and the x-axis.

Matrices

Order: $\begin{pmatrix} 2 & 4 & 5 \\ 3 & 7 & 1 \end{pmatrix}$ is a 2 × 3 matrix (2 rows, 3 columns)

Addition: $\begin{pmatrix} 5 & 3 & 0 \\ 2 & -1 & 4 \end{pmatrix} + \begin{pmatrix} 1 & 4 & 6 \\ 0 & 3 & -5 \end{pmatrix} = \begin{pmatrix} 6 & 7 & 6 \\ 2 & 2 & -1 \end{pmatrix}$

Multiplication: $\begin{pmatrix} 3 & 5 \\ 2 & 4 \end{pmatrix} \begin{pmatrix} 6 & 1 \\ 7 & 8 \end{pmatrix} = \begin{pmatrix} 3\times6+5\times7 & 3\times1+5\times8 \\ 2\times6+4\times7 & 2\times1+4\times8 \end{pmatrix} = \begin{pmatrix} 53 & 43 \\ 40 & 34 \end{pmatrix}$

Multiplication by a scalar: $3\begin{pmatrix} 2 & 1 \\ 5 & 4 \end{pmatrix} = \begin{pmatrix} 6 & 3 \\ 15 & 12 \end{pmatrix}$

Unit (or identity) matrix (2 × 2): $I = \begin{pmatrix} 1 & 0 \\ 0 & 1 \end{pmatrix}$ IM = M and MI = M

Zero (or null) matrix (2 × 2): $O = \begin{pmatrix} 0 & 0 \\ 0 & 0 \end{pmatrix}$ OM = O and MO = O
$\qquad$ O + M = M and M + O = M

The determinant of $\begin{pmatrix} 3 & 4 \\ 5 & 8 \end{pmatrix}$ is $3\times8 - 4\times5 = 24 - 20 = 4$

Inverse: if M^{-1} is the inverse of M then $MM^{-1} = I$ and $M^{-1}M = I$

If $M = \begin{pmatrix} 7 & -6 \\ 3 & -2 \end{pmatrix}$ then $M^{-1} = \frac{1}{4}\begin{pmatrix} -2 & 6 \\ -3 & 7 \end{pmatrix} = \begin{pmatrix} -\frac{1}{2} & \frac{3}{2} \\ -\frac{3}{4} & \frac{7}{4} \end{pmatrix}$

(We change the positions of the 7 and -2, change the signs of the 3 and -6 and divide by the determinant, 4.)

A matrix with zero determinant has no inverse. It is called a **singular** matrix.

Solution of simultaneous equation

We can write the equations $\begin{array}{c} 7x - 6y = 1 \\ 3x - 2y = 5 \end{array}$ as $\begin{pmatrix} 7 & -6 \\ 3 & -2 \end{pmatrix} \begin{pmatrix} x \\ y \end{pmatrix} = \begin{pmatrix} 1 \\ 5 \end{pmatrix}$

Premultiplying both sides by the inverse of the first matrix,

$\begin{pmatrix} -\frac{1}{2} & \frac{3}{2} \\ -\frac{3}{4} & \frac{7}{4} \end{pmatrix} \begin{pmatrix} 7 & -6 \\ 3 & -2 \end{pmatrix} \begin{pmatrix} x \\ y \end{pmatrix} = \begin{pmatrix} -\frac{1}{2} & \frac{3}{2} \\ -\frac{3}{4} & \frac{7}{4} \end{pmatrix} \begin{pmatrix} 1 \\ 5 \end{pmatrix}$

$\begin{pmatrix} 1 & 0 \\ 0 & 1 \end{pmatrix} \begin{pmatrix} x \\ y \end{pmatrix} = \begin{pmatrix} -\frac{1}{2} + \frac{15}{2} \\ -\frac{3}{4} + \frac{35}{4} \end{pmatrix} = \begin{pmatrix} 7 \\ 8 \end{pmatrix}$

$\begin{pmatrix} x \\ y \end{pmatrix} = \begin{pmatrix} 7 \\ 8 \end{pmatrix}$ $x = 7$ and $y = 8$

Exercise 46

1. If $A = \begin{pmatrix} 5 & 2 \\ 7 & 4 \end{pmatrix}$ and $B = \begin{pmatrix} 3 & 0 \\ 6 & 1 \end{pmatrix}$, find $A + B$, $3A$, $A - B$, AB and BA. Is $AB = BA$?

2. If $P = \begin{pmatrix} 2 & -1 \\ 0 & 1 \end{pmatrix}$ and $Q = \begin{pmatrix} 3 & 2 \\ -1 & 0 \end{pmatrix}$, find $P + Q$, $5P$, $P - Q$, PQ and P^2.

3. $C = \begin{pmatrix} 1 & 2 \\ -1 & 1 \\ 0 & 3 \end{pmatrix}$, $D = \begin{pmatrix} 2 & -1 & 3 \\ 1 & 0 & 1 \end{pmatrix}$, $E = \begin{pmatrix} -1 & 3 \\ 0 & 2 \end{pmatrix}$.

   Calculate, where possible (a) CD (b) DC (c) CE (d) EC (e) DE (f) ED

4. (a) If $MP = M$, what is P? (b) If $M + Q = M$, what is Q?

5. Simplify, where possible,

   (a) $\begin{pmatrix} 2 \\ 3 \end{pmatrix} \begin{pmatrix} 1 & 2 \\ 3 & 4 \end{pmatrix}$ (b) $(2 \ 3) \begin{pmatrix} 1 & 2 \\ 3 & 4 \end{pmatrix}$ (c) $\begin{pmatrix} 1 & 2 \\ 3 & 4 \end{pmatrix} (2 \ 3)$ (d) $\begin{pmatrix} 1 & 2 \\ 3 & 4 \end{pmatrix} \begin{pmatrix} 2 \\ 3 \end{pmatrix}$

6. $A = \begin{pmatrix} -1 & 3 \\ 2 & 4 \end{pmatrix}$ and $B = \begin{pmatrix} 3 & -4 \\ -5 & 6 \end{pmatrix}$. Solve the equations

   (a) $X + A = B$ (b) $Y + B = 3A$

7. (a) Find a, such that $(3 \ 5) \begin{pmatrix} 4 \\ a \end{pmatrix} = (22)$ (b) Find b and c such that

   $\begin{pmatrix} 1 & b \\ c & 2 \end{pmatrix} \begin{pmatrix} 2 \\ 4 \end{pmatrix} = \begin{pmatrix} 14 \\ 16 \end{pmatrix}$

8. (a) Evaluate (i) $\begin{pmatrix} 7 & 3 \\ 2 & 1 \end{pmatrix} \begin{pmatrix} 1 & -3 \\ -2 & 7 \end{pmatrix}$ (ii) $\begin{pmatrix} 5 & 2 \\ 6 & 3 \end{pmatrix} \begin{pmatrix} 3 & -2 \\ -6 & 5 \end{pmatrix}$

   (b) Find the inverses of each of the following and check your answer by multiplication:

   (i) $\begin{pmatrix} 3 & 5 \\ 1 & 2 \end{pmatrix}$ (ii) $\begin{pmatrix} 3 & 7 \\ 2 & 5 \end{pmatrix}$ (iii) $\begin{pmatrix} 1 & 3 \\ 0 & 1 \end{pmatrix}$ (iv) $\begin{pmatrix} 4 & -3 \\ -1 & 1 \end{pmatrix}$

9. State the condition for $\begin{pmatrix} a & b \\ c & d \end{pmatrix}$ to be singular. Find, where possible, the inverses of the following and check by multiplication:

   (a) $\begin{pmatrix} 3 & 2 \\ 5 & 4 \end{pmatrix}$ (b) $\begin{pmatrix} 9 & 6 \\ 3 & 2 \end{pmatrix}$ (c) $\begin{pmatrix} 4 & 3 \\ 2 & 1 \end{pmatrix}$ (d) $\begin{pmatrix} -1 & 3 \\ 2 & -2 \end{pmatrix}$

10. (a) Find the determinant of $\begin{pmatrix} 6 & 7 \\ 3 & 4 \end{pmatrix}$ and of $\begin{pmatrix} 2 & 3 \\ 1 & -1 \end{pmatrix}$

    (b) State in its simplest form, the determinant of $\begin{pmatrix} k+2 & 5 \\ 3 & k \end{pmatrix}$.
    Find the values of k for which the matrix is singular.

11. State (a) the determinant (b) the inverse of $\begin{pmatrix} 4 & 2 \\ 5 & 3 \end{pmatrix}$.
    Solve $\begin{pmatrix} 4 & 2 \\ 5 & 3 \end{pmatrix} \begin{pmatrix} x \\ y \end{pmatrix} = \begin{pmatrix} 7 \\ 8 \end{pmatrix}$

12. Solve (a) $\begin{pmatrix} 3 & -4 \\ 1 & -2 \end{pmatrix} \begin{pmatrix} x \\ y \end{pmatrix} = \begin{pmatrix} 1 \\ -1 \end{pmatrix}$ (b) $\begin{pmatrix} 1 & -3 \\ 2 & 1 \end{pmatrix} \begin{pmatrix} x \\ y \end{pmatrix} = \begin{pmatrix} 6 \\ 5 \end{pmatrix}$

13. Write the following equations in matrix from and solve them:
   (a) $3x + 7y = 5$ (b) $5u - 7w = 5$
       $2x + 5y = 4$ $3u - 4w = 2$

   (c) $4n + p = 1$ (d) $7c + 3d = 13$
       $5n + 2p = 5$ $c - d = 4$

Binary operations

$2 \times 3 = 6$; $7 - 4 = 3$; $A \cap B = C$ (for sets). These are examples of binary operations. Two elements are combined to give a single element.

Let S be a set and $*$ be a binary operation. Suppose that x and y are elements of S and that when they are combined by the operation we obtain z. Then we can write $x * y = z$. If z is always an element of S, whatever elements are used as x and y, then the set S is said to be **closed** under the operation $*$.

The operation is **commutative** if $x * y = y * x$ for all elements of S.

There is an **identity element**, I, if $x * I = x$ and $I * x = x$ for every element x of S.

If $x * a = I$ and $a * x = I$, then a is the **inverse** of x.

Exercise 47

1. (a) Let $S = \{0, 1, 2, 3, 4, \ldots\}$. Give an example to show that S is not closed under subtraction and one to show that it is not closed under division. Is it closed under (i) addition (ii) multiplication?
   (b) Let $T = \{\ldots -4, -3, -2, -1, 0, 1, 2, 3, 4, \ldots\}$. Is T closed under (i) subtraction (ii) division?

2. Which of the following are commutative operations for real numbers: addition, subtraction, multiplication, division? Illustrate by using the numbers 2 and 6.

3. Use the set $\{0, 1, 2, 3, \ldots\}$ and the operation $*$ where $a * b = a + b - 6$. Find $9 * 2$, $2 * 9$, $3 * 1$, $1 * 3$. Is the set closed under the operation $*$? Is $*$ commutative?

4. Use the set $\{0, 1, 2, 3, \ldots\}$ and the operation $\sim$ 'difference' which means 'take the smaller number from the larger'. Thus $5 \sim 3 = 2$ and $6 \sim 9 = 3$. Find $9 \sim 6$, $3 \sim 5$, $16 \sim 9$, $9 \sim 16$. Is the set closed? Is the operation commutative?

5. (a) State the identity element for (i) addition (ii) multiplication. Give two examples to illustrate each.

(b) $5 + (-5) = 0$. What is the inverse of 5 for addition? What are the inverses of 7, 11 and -4 for addition?

(c) If $3 \times n = 1$, what is n? What are the inverses of $3, 5, \frac{1}{4}$ and $\frac{3}{7}$ for multiplication?

6.

$\times$	2	4	6	8
2			6	
4			2	
6				
8				

The operation $\times$ on the set A = $\{2, 4, 6, 8\}$ means 'take the remainder when $a \times b$ is divided by 10. For example, $2 \times 8 = 6$ and $4 \times 8 = 2$. Copy and complete the table. (a) Is A closed under $\times$? (b) Is $\times$ commutative? (c) State the identity element. (d) State the inverse of each element.

7. Repeat question 6 using B = $\{1, 3, 5, 7, 9\}$ instead of A. (One of the elements has no inverse.)

8. The operation $\sim$ on the set $\{0, 1, 2, 3\}$ is defined as in question 4. Draw up a table as above. (a) State the identity element. (b) State the inverse of each element. (c) What is x if $x \sim 2 = 1$?

9. Take $\{-2, 0, 2\}$ and the operation $*$ defined by $a * b = \frac{1}{2}(a + b)$. Draw up a table as above. (a) Is the set closed under $*$? (b) Is there an identity element? (c) Is the operation commutative?

10. A = $\begin{pmatrix} -1 & 0 \\ 0 & -1 \end{pmatrix}$, B = $\begin{pmatrix} 0 & 1 \\ -1 & 0 \end{pmatrix}$, C = $\begin{pmatrix} 0 & -1 \\ 1 & 0 \end{pmatrix}$, D = $\begin{pmatrix} 1 & 0 \\ 0 & 1 \end{pmatrix}$.

Draw up a table for multiplication of these matrices. Is $\{A, B, C, D\}$ closed under multiplication? State the identity element and the inverse of each element.

11. Take $\{$ integers $\}$ and the operation ∇ as defined by $x \nabla y = x + y + xy$. Calculate $3 \nabla 5, 2 \nabla 3, (-7) \nabla 1, (-2) \nabla (-3)$. Solve (a) $4 \nabla n = 19$ (b) $(-4) \nabla m = -7$.

12. (a) Calculate $(9 + 5) + 3$ and $9 + (5 + 3)$. If an operation $*$ is such that $(a * b) * c = a * (b * c)$ for all elements of a set then $*$ is said to be **associative**. Is addition associative?

(b) Calculate $9 - (5 - 3)$ and $(9 - 5) - 3$. Is subtraction associative?

(c) Calculate $20 \div (10 \div 2)$ and $(20 \div 10) \div 2$. Is division associative?

(d) Use the numbers 5, 3 and 2 to show that multiplication is associative.

13. Δ is defined by $a \Delta b = 3a - b$.

(a) Calculate $5 \Delta 2, 2 \Delta 5, 7 \Delta 3, 3 \Delta 7$; Is the operation commutative?

(b) Calculate $(5 \Delta 2) \Delta 3$ and $5 \Delta (2 \Delta 3)$. Is the operation associative?

14. Operation $^\circ$ is defined by $x ^\circ y = x + y - 2$.

(a) Evaluate $8 ^\circ 5, 5 ^\circ 8, (8 ^\circ 5) ^\circ 4$ and $8 ^\circ (5 ^\circ 4)$.

(b) $(a ^\circ b) ^\circ c = (a + b - 2) ^\circ c = (a + b - 2) + c - 2 = a + b + c - 4$. Simplify $a ^\circ (b ^\circ c)$ in this way. Is the operation associative?

(c) Find x if $3 ^\circ x = 10$.

15.

*	p	q	r	s
p	r	s	p	q
q	s	p	q	r
r	p	q	r	s
s	q	r	s	p

The table is for the operation * on the set
{ p, q, r, s }.
(a) State the identity element.
(b) State the inverse of each element.

(c) The operation is commutative. Give an example of this.
(d) State the value of $p * (q * s)$ and of $(p * q) * s$. What property
does this illustrate?

Angles

Exercise 48

1. An acute angle is less than $90°$. Describe in this way (a) an obtuse
   angle (b) a reflex angle (c) a right angle. Draw an example of each type
   of angle.
2. (a) Draw a diagram to show a pair of supplementary angles.
   (b) Draw a diagram to show a pair of vertically opposite angles.
3. (a) Draw two parallel lines, cut be a transversal. Mark a pair of corresponding angles. For parallel lines, corresponding angles are equal.
   (b) Draw another pair of parallel lines and a transversal and mark a
   pair of alternate angles. Make a statement as in (a).
   (c) Draw a third pair of parallel lines and a transversal. Mark two interior angles on the same side of the transversal. Make a statement as
   in (a).
4. Through what angle does the minute hand of a clock turn in (a) 10
   minutes (b) 25 minutes (c) $\frac{3}{4}$ hour?
5. Through what angle does the hour hand of a clock turn in (a) 3 hours
   (b) 4 hours (c) $\frac{1}{2}$ hour?
6. State the angle between the two hands of a clock at (a) 2 o'clock (b)
   3.30 (c) 10.30
7. Draw a diagram to show the following bearings:
   (a) $060°$ (b) $170°$ (c) $280°$
8. State (in the form $275°$) the direction you are facing after each of the
   following (a) Face east. Turn $30°$ clockwise. (b) Face south. Turn $70°$
   anticlockwise. (c) Face west. Turn $10°$ anti- clockwise. (d) Face west.
   Turn $130°$ clockwise.

9. In Fig. 1, (a) if $a = 50°$ and $b = 65°$, find c.
(b) if $b = 80°$ and $a = c$, find a.
(c) if $b = a + c$, find b.

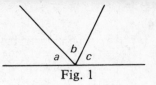

Fig. 1

10. In Fig. 2, (a) if $p = 80°$, $q = 70°$ and $r = 110°$, find s.
(b) if $p = 70°$, $q = 60°$ and $r = s$, find r.

11. In Fig. 2, let the four lines meet at C. What can be said about G, C and K if $q + r = 180°$?

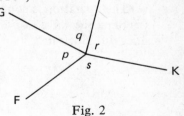

Fig. 2

12. In Fig. 3,
(a) Name a pair of corresponding angles.
(b) Name a pair of alternate angles.
(c) Name a pair of vertically opposite angles.
(d) If $y = 75°$, calculate u.

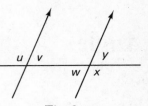

Fig. 3

In Questions **13**, **14** and **15**, calculate the sizes of the angles a, b, c, etc. Give reasons for your statements.

13.

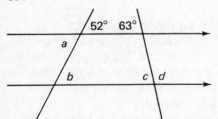

Fig. 4

14.

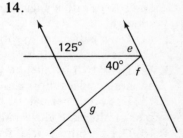

Fig. 5

15.

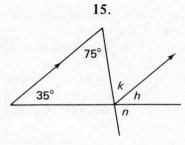

Fig. 6

Triangles and polygons

Exercise 49

1. Describe the following types of triangle and draw an example of each:
   - (a) acute-angled triangles
   - (b) right-angled triangles
   - (c) obtuse-angled triangles
   - (d) isosceles triangles
   - (e) equilateral triangles
   - (f) scalene triangles

2. In Fig. 1:
   - (a) If $a = 70°$ and $b = 55°$, calculate c.
   - (b) If $b = 84°$ and $c = 48°$, calculate a.
   - (c) If $a = 90°$, state the value of $b + c$.

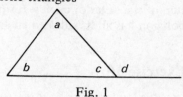

Fig. 1

3. (a) State the relationship between the angles a, b and d in Fig. 1.
   - (b) If $a = 80°$ and $b = 60°$, what is d?
   - (c) If $b = 65°$ and $d = 135°$, what is a?

4. In Fig. 2, PQ = PR.
   - (a) What type of triangle is PQR?
   - (b) If $y = 64°$, calculate z and x.
   - (c) If $x = 30°$, calculate y.
   - (d) If $x = 60°$, calculate y. What type of triangle is PQR in this case?

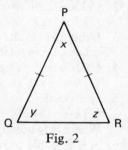

Fig. 2

5. Is it possible to have a triangle with angles of
   (a) $70°, 36°, 74°$ (b) $85°, 55°, 60°$ (c) $160°, 15°, 5°$?

Calculate the angles a, b, c, etc., giving reasons:

6.

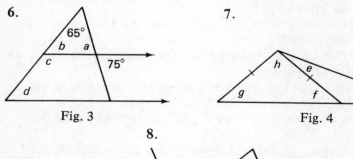

Fig. 3

7.

Fig. 4

8.

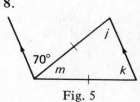

Fig. 5

57

9. In △ ABC, AB = AC and BÂC = 44°. D is a point on AC such that BD bisects AB̂C. Calculate CB̂D and BD̂C.
10. Draw square PQRS and equilateral traingle PQT so that T is inside the square. Join RT and ST. Calculate TQ̂R, QT̂R and ST̂R.
11. In △ GHK, GĤK = 90°. T is a point on GK such that HT̂G = 90°.
   (a) If HĜK = 35°, calculate GĤT and HK̂T.
   (b) Show that, whatever the size of HĜK, GĤT = HK̂T.

Polygons

The sum of the interior angles of a polygon of n sides is $(n - 2) \times 180°$. The sum of the exterior angles, formed by producing the sides, is 360°. **A regular** polygon has all its sides equal and all its angles equal.

Exercise 50

1. Calculate the sum of the interior angles of a polygon having
   (a) 5 sides (b) 8 sides (c) 10 sides (d) 24 sides.
2. Calculate the size of each exterior angle of a regular polygon having
   (a) 5 sides (b) 6 sides (c) 10 sides (d) 12 sides.
3. Using the results of question 2, calculate the size of each interior angle of a regular polygon having (a) 5 (b) 6 (c) 10 (d) 12 sides.
4. Calculate the size of each interior angle of a regular polygon having
   (a) 9 sides (b) 8 sides (c) 15 sides (d) 7 sides
5. Is it possible to have a regular polygon with an exterior angle of
   (a) 60° (b) 50° (c) 45° (d) 40° (e) 30°?
   Where it is possible, state the number of sides.
6. Is it possible to have a regular polygon with an interior angle of
   (a) 120° (b) 100° (c) 160° (d) 145°?
   Where it is possible, state the number of sides.
7. How many sides has (a) a pentagon (b) a hexagon (c) an octagon?
8. A pentagon has interior angles of 100°, 110°, 115° and 125°. What is the size of the other angle?
9. A hexagon has angles of 70°, 80°, 125°, 140° and 165°. What is the size of the other angle?
10. Six angles of an octagon are each 130°. The remaining two angles are equal. Find the size of each.
11. State the sum of the four angles of a quadrilateral. If three of the angles are 100°, 95° and 85°, calculate the fourth.
12. If the angles of a quadrilateral are $x°$, $2x°$, $3x°$ and $4x°$, state the value of x.
13. ABCDE is a regular pentagon. Calculate the angles of triangle ABD.
14. PQRSTV is a regular hexagon. Calculate the angles of triangle PRS.

Symmetry

Bilateral (or line) symmetry
In Fig. 1, PQ is the axis of symmetry. If folded
about PQ, the triangle ABD fits onto triangle
CBD and K onto L. If PQ is regarded as a mirror,
L is the image of K and C of A. Notice that KL
is perpendicular to PQ and that PQ bisects KL.
K and L are equidistant from PQ.
A three dimensional shape can have symmetry
about a plane. If H is the image of G, then GH is
perpendicular to the plane and G and H are equidistant from the plane.

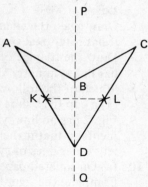

Fig. 1

Rotational symmetry
If the shape in Fig. 2 is rotated through 120° about
the centre it looks exactly the same. It has rotational symmetry of order 3 because 360°/120° = 3.
    The shape in Fig. 3 has rotational symmetry of
order 4. It can also be said to have point symmetry.
Q is the reflection of P in O: S is the reflection of
R in O.

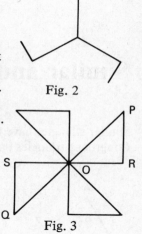

Fig. 2

Fig. 3

Exercise 51

1. Sketch the following figures and mark their axes of symmetry with
   broken lines. (A figure may have more than one axis.) (a) an
   isosceles triangle (b) an equilateral triangle (c) a kite (d) a rectangle
   (e) a square (f) a regular pentagon (5 sides).
2. On squared paper draw the capital letters S, A, E, H and N. Show any
   axes of symmetry with broken lines.
3. The capital letter Z has rotational symmetry. Which other capital
   letters have rotational symmetry? Draw each and mark its centre of
   symmetry.
4. State the order of rotational symmetry of (a) an equilateral triangle
   (b) a parallelogram (c) a rectangle (d) a square (e) a regular pentagon
   (f) a circle. Which has no line symmetry?

5. On squared paper, using axes marked from -3 to $+3$, mark the points $(0, 2)$, $(0, 3)$ and $(2, 3)$ and join them to form a triangle. Complete the figure so that it is symmetrical about both the x-axis and the y-axis.

6. Draw again the triangle of question **5** and complete the figure so that it has rotational symmetry of order 4 about O.

7. Draw the triangle of question **5** again and complete the figure so that it has line symmetry about both $y = x$ and $y = -x$.

8. Which of the following objects have symmetry about a plane: (a) a cup (b) a shoe (c) a cube (d) a desk.

9. Fig. 2 has no line symmetry. Copy it and add three more line segments so that it then has symmetry about a line. Show this line and any other lines of symmetry.

10. (a) On squared paper join $(2, 1)$ to $(1, 1)$ and join $(1, 1)$ to $(1, 3)$. Complete the figure so that it has point symmetry about the origin.
    (b) Draw again the L of (a) and complete the figure so that it has point symmetry about $(0, 2)$

Similar and congruent triangles

Similar triangles have the same shape. They are usually different sizes. Congruent triangles have the same size as well as the same shape.

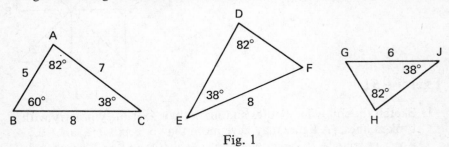

Fig. 1

$\triangle$DEF is congruent to $\triangle$ABC and so DF = 5, DE = 7 and $\hat{F} = 60°$. $\triangle$HGJ is similar to $\triangle$ABC. GJ and BC are corresponding sides because both are opposite 82°.

$\dfrac{GJ}{BC} = \dfrac{6}{8} = \dfrac{3}{4}$. $\therefore \dfrac{GH}{BA} = \frac{3}{4}$. GH $= \frac{3}{4}$BA $= \frac{3}{4} \times 5 = 3\frac{3}{4}$.

Similarly $\dfrac{HJ}{AC} = \frac{3}{4}$, HJ $= \frac{3}{4}$AC $= \frac{3}{4} \times 7 = 5\frac{1}{4}$.

60

Exercise 52

1. Calculate a and b.

2. Calculate c and d.

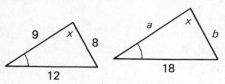
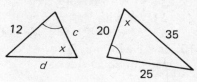

Fig. 2

Fig. 3

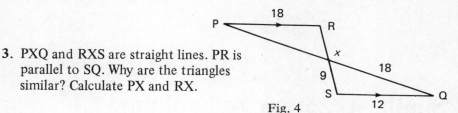

3. PXQ and RXS are straight lines. PR is parallel to SQ. Why are the triangles similar? Calculate PX and RX.

Fig. 4

4. ABCD is a trapezium with AB parallel to CD. Diagonals AC and BD cut at E. Name a pair of similar triangles. If AB = 6 cm, BC = 8 cm, CD = 18 cm, BE = 4 cm and CE = 9 cm, calculate as many lengths as possible.

5. PN is an altitude of $\triangle$PQR. Prove $\triangle$s PQN and PNR are similar. Copy and complete $\dfrac{h}{b} = -$ and hence $h^2 = \ldots$.
If $b = 9$ and $c = 4$, calculate h.

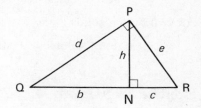

Fig. 5

6. (a) Name a triangle similar to $\triangle$ACE. Calculate BD.
(b) Name a triangle similar to $\triangle$AEF. Calculate EF and FD.

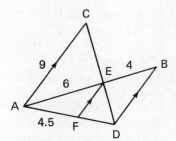

Fig. 6

7. State the four tests for the congruency of triangles. Illustrate each with a figure.

8. By making freehand sketches, find which of the following triangles are congruent:
$\triangle$ABC with AB = 5 cm, AC = 6 cm, $\hat{A}$ = 43°
$\triangle$DEF with DF = 5 cm, DE = 6 cm, $\hat{D}$ = 43°
$\triangle$GHJ with HJ = 5 cm, GH = 6 cm, $\hat{G}$ = 43°
$\triangle$KLM with KL = 5 cm, LM = 6 cm, $\hat{L}$ = 43°

9. By making freehand sketches, find which of the following triangles are congruent:
   $\triangle$NPQ with $\hat{N} = 54°$, $\hat{P} = 77°$, NP = 8 cm
   $\triangle$RST with $\hat{R} = 49°$, $\hat{T} = 77°$, ST = 8 cm
   $\triangle$UVW with $\hat{W} = 77°$, $\hat{V} = 54°$, UW = 8 cm
   $\triangle$XYZ with $\hat{X} = 54°$, $\hat{Y} = 49°$, XZ = 8 cm
10. In $\triangle$s ABC and DEF, $\hat{A} = \hat{F}$, $\hat{B} = \hat{E}$ and BC = DE. Name the other pairs of equal sides.

Similarity: areas and volumes

For two similar plane figures:

$$\text{ratio of areas} = (\text{ratio of corresponding sides})^2$$

For two similar solids:

$$\text{ratio of volumes} = (\text{ratio of corresponding sides})^3$$

Exercise 53

1. In rectangle ABCD, AB = 5 cm and BC = 4 cm. In rectangle PQRS, PQ = 15 cm and QR = 12 cm. Calculate the area of each rectangle. State, in their simplest forms, (a) PQ : AB (b) QR : BC (c) area of PQRS : area of ABCD.
   Are the rectangles similar? Check that ratio of areas = (ratio of lengths)^2.
2. In $\triangle$ HJK, HJ = 9 cm, JK = 12 cm and J = 90°. In $\triangle$LMN, LM = 6 cm, MN = 8 cm and M = 90°. Calculate the area of each triangle. State, in their simplest forms, (a) HJ : LM (b) JK : MN (c) area of HJK : area of LMN.
   Are the triangles similar? Check that ratio of areas = (ratio of lengths)^2.
3. Triangle I has a base of 8 cm and an area of 24 cm^2. Triangle II is similar to triangle I and has a base of 6 cm. Calculate (a) the ratio of the bases (b) the ratio of the areas (c) the area of triangle II.
4. A circle has an area of 10 cm^2. What is the area of a circle of (a) twice (b) half this radius?
5. Two circular discs of the same thickness and material have diameters of

15 cm and 6 cm. State, in their simplest forms, the ratios of (a) the diameters (b) the areas (c) the masses. If the large disc has a mass of 150 g, what is the mass of the small disc?

6. On a small photograph, a building is 4 cm high and its area is 12 cm². On an enlargement, the building is 14 cm high. What is its area?

7. A cuboid has measurements of 18 cm, 15 cm and 9 cm. A second cuboid has measurements of 6 cm, 5 cm and 3 cm. Show that the cuboids are similar. Find the volume of each and hence find the ratio of the volumes. Check that ratio of volumes = (ratio of corresponding edges)².

8. Two cuboids are similar. The ratio of their heights is 3 : 2. What is the ratio of their volumes? The volume of the smaller one is 72 cm³. What is the volume of the larger one?

9. The volume of a cube is 12 cm³. What is the volume of a cube having an edge of twice the length?

10. The volume of a sphere is 54 cm³. What is the volume of a sphere of $\frac{1}{3}$ the diameter?

11. A sphere has a diameter of 12 cm and a second sphere has a diameter of 8 cm. State, in their simplest forms, the ratios of (a) the diameters (b) the surface areas (c) the volumes.

12. A cylindrical tin has a diameter of 8 cm and a height of 12 cm and contains 320 g of powder. A second tin has the same shape but its diameter is 6 cm. Calculate for the second tin (a) its height (b) the mass of powder it can hold.

13. A wooden cone has a height of 12 cm and a base radius of 7 cm. Calculate its volume using $3\frac{1}{7}$ for π. A cut is made parallel to the base so that it divides the original cone into a small cone of height 6 cm and a part called a frustum. Calculate the volume of the small cone and of the frustum.

Special quadrilaterals

Exercise 54

1. Draw an example of each of the following quadrilaterals: parallelogram, rectangle, square, rhombus, kite and trapezium.

2. ABCD is a parallelogram.
   (a) If AB = 9 cm and BC = 6 cm, state the lengths of CD and DA.
   (b) If $\hat{A} = 50°$, state the sizes of $\hat{B}$, $\hat{C}$ and $\hat{D}$.

(c) If diagonals AC and BD intersect at E and AC = 12 cm and BD = 7 cm, state the lengths of AE and BE.

3. In Fig. 1, PQRS is a rhombus. Equal lengths are marked.
   (a) Name the two axes of symmetry.
   (b) State the size of PT̂Q.
   (c) If PQ̂T = 55°, state the sizes of RQ̂T, QP̂T and PŜT.

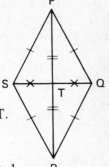

Fig. 1

4. The diagonals of rectangle GHJK intersect at M and GĤM = 25°. Draw a diagram and mark all equal lengths. Also enter the sizes of all the angles.

5. Draw a square VWXY and its diagonals VX and WY intersecting at N.
   (a) Name all equal lengths. (b) Enter the sizes of all the angles.

6. Draw a kite DEFG with DE = DG and FE = FG. Draw the diagonals and let H be their point of intersection.
   (a) Name the axis of symmetry.
   (b) State the size of DĤG.
   (c) Mark all equal lengths.
   (d) If GD̂E = 130° and GF̂E = 40°, state the sizes of GD̂F, GF̂D and DĜF.

7. PQRS is a quadrilateral. State the type of quadrilateral if (a) PQ = QR and PS = SR (b) P̂ = R̂ and Q̂ = Ŝ (c) P̂ = Q̂ = R̂ = Ŝ.

8. WXYZ is a parallelogram. State the type of parallelogram if
   (a) Ŵ = 90° (b) WX = XY (c) WY = XZ (d) WY cuts XZ at 90°.

9. P = {all parallelograms}, H = {all rhombuses}, R = {all rectangles}. Draw a Venn diagram showing the three sets. Describe R ∩ H.

10. Fig. 2 shows how to construct the mediator (perpendicular bisector) of a line CD. With centres C and D and equal radii, draw arcs to intersect as shown at P and Q. What kind of quadrilateral is CPDQ? Use this to explain why PQ is the mediator of CD. Carry out the construction taking CD as 7 cm. Check that CM = MD and CM̂P = 90°.

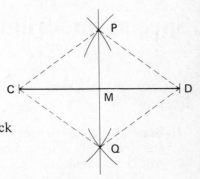

Fig. 2

11. Fig. 3 shows how to construct the line bisecting $\hat{AOB}$. With centre O, draw an arc cutting OA at E and OB at F. With centres E and F and equal radii, draw arcs intersecting at H. What kind of quadrilateral is OEHF? Use this to explain why OH bisects $\hat{AOB}$. Carry out the construction with $\hat{AOB} = 50°$ and check that $\hat{AOH} = \hat{BOH}$.

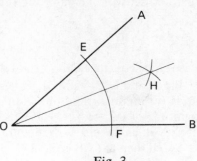

Fig. 3

Vectors

A **vector** quantity has magnitude and direction. Examples: displacements, velocities, forces.
A **scalar** quantity has magnitude only. Examples: distance, mass, temperature.
A vector can be represented by a line segment showing its direction and using a length on a suitable scale for its magnitude.

$$\vec{PQ} = \begin{pmatrix} 4 \\ 2 \end{pmatrix}, \quad \vec{QR} = \begin{pmatrix} -1 \\ 3 \end{pmatrix}$$

Equal vectors

$\vec{PQ}$, $\vec{VW}$ and $\vec{SU}$ are equal vectors.
If $\vec{PQ} = \mathbf{a}$, then $\vec{VW} = \mathbf{a}$ and $\vec{SU} = \mathbf{a}$.

Multiplication by a scalar

$$\vec{XY} = \tfrac{1}{2}\vec{PQ} = \tfrac{1}{2}\mathbf{a} = \tfrac{1}{2}\begin{pmatrix} 4 \\ 2 \end{pmatrix} = \begin{pmatrix} 2 \\ 1 \end{pmatrix}.$$

$$\vec{UT} = -\vec{QR} = -\mathbf{b} = -\begin{pmatrix} -1 \\ 3 \end{pmatrix}$$

$$= \begin{pmatrix} 1 \\ -3 \end{pmatrix}.$$

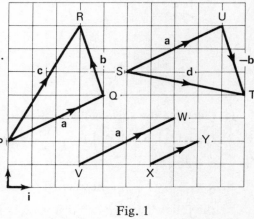

Fig. 1

Sum of two vectors

$$\vec{PQ} + \vec{QR} = \vec{PR}, \quad \mathbf{a} + \mathbf{b} = \mathbf{c}, \quad \begin{pmatrix} 4 \\ 2 \end{pmatrix} + \begin{pmatrix} -1 \\ 3 \end{pmatrix} = \begin{pmatrix} 3 \\ 5 \end{pmatrix}.$$

Difference of two vectors

$$\vec{SU} - \vec{TU} = \vec{SU} + (-\vec{TU}) = \vec{SU} + \vec{UT} = \vec{ST},$$

$$\mathbf{a} - \mathbf{b} = \mathbf{d}, \quad \begin{pmatrix} 4 \\ 2 \end{pmatrix} - \begin{pmatrix} -1 \\ 3 \end{pmatrix} = \begin{pmatrix} 5 \\ -1 \end{pmatrix}$$

Base Vectors: Let **i** and **j** be unit vectors as shown in Fig. 1.

$\mathbf{i} = \begin{pmatrix} 1 \\ 0 \end{pmatrix}$ and $\mathbf{j} = \begin{pmatrix} 0 \\ 1 \end{pmatrix}$.

Any vector in the plane can be expressed in terms of **i** and **j**.

e.g. $\mathbf{a} = 4\mathbf{i} + 2\mathbf{j}$ and $\mathbf{b} = -\mathbf{i}$ and $3\mathbf{j}$.

Magnitude (or **modulus**) and **direction** of a vector: By Pythagoras' theorem, the magnitude of $\vec{PQ} = \sqrt{(4^2 + 2^2)} = \sqrt{20} \simeq 4.47$

If $\vec{PQ}$ makes an angle of θ with the direction of **i**, $\tan \theta = \frac{2}{4} = 0.5, \theta \simeq 26.6°$.

If $\vec{AB} = 3\ \vec{CD}$, then (1) AB is parallel to CD and (2) the length of AB = 3 × the length of CD.

If $\vec{EF} = k\ \vec{FG}$, then E, F and G are collinear (in a straight line).

Exercise 55

1. Express in the form $\begin{pmatrix} x \\ y \end{pmatrix}$: $\vec{AB}, \vec{BE}, \vec{DC}, \vec{CB}, \vec{CE}$.

2. Express in the form $a\mathbf{i} + b\mathbf{j}$: $\vec{AC}, \vec{BD}, \vec{DA}, \vec{BC}, \vec{DE}$.

3. If $\vec{EC} = k\ \vec{AB}$, what is k? Write down a relation between $\vec{BC}$ and $\vec{ED}$.

4. Name a single vector equal to (a) $\vec{AB} + \vec{BC}$
   (b) $\vec{EC} + \vec{CD}$ (c) $\vec{EA} + \vec{AD}$ (d) $\vec{AB} + \vec{BC} + \vec{CD}$.

5. Find the magnitude of (a) $\vec{CD}$ (b) $\vec{BD}$ (c) $\vec{DA}$.

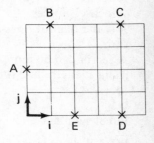

Fig. 2

6. Calculate the angle between the direction of BD and **i**.

7. If $\mathbf{a} = \begin{pmatrix} 3 \\ 5 \end{pmatrix}$, $\mathbf{b} = \begin{pmatrix} 2 \\ -3 \end{pmatrix}$, $\mathbf{c} = \begin{pmatrix} -6 \\ 4 \end{pmatrix}$, calculate $\mathbf{a} + \mathbf{b}$, $\mathbf{a} - \mathbf{b}$, $3\mathbf{b}$, $\frac{1}{2}\mathbf{c}$, $2\mathbf{a} + \mathbf{c}$, $\mathbf{c} - 2\mathbf{b}$.

8. $\mathbf{x} = \begin{pmatrix} 3 \\ 1 \end{pmatrix}$, $\mathbf{y} = \begin{pmatrix} 1 \\ 2 \end{pmatrix}$. On squared paper show a single vector for each of the following: $2\mathbf{y}$, $-\mathbf{x}$, $\mathbf{x} + \mathbf{y}$, $\mathbf{x} - \mathbf{y}$, $2\mathbf{x} + 3\mathbf{y}$.

9. If $\mathbf{u} = \begin{pmatrix} 2 \\ 3 \end{pmatrix}$, which of the following vectors are parallel to **u**

   (a) $\begin{pmatrix} 3 \\ 2 \end{pmatrix}$ (b) $\begin{pmatrix} 6 \\ 9 \end{pmatrix}$ (c) $\begin{pmatrix} 4 \\ -6 \end{pmatrix}$ (d) $\begin{pmatrix} 1 \\ 1\frac{1}{2} \end{pmatrix}$ (e) $\begin{pmatrix} -14 \\ -21 \end{pmatrix}$?
   Express those parallel to **u** in the form $k\ \mathbf{u}$.

10. A, B, C, D are points such that $\vec{AB} = \begin{pmatrix} 5 \\ -1 \end{pmatrix}$, $\vec{AC} = \begin{pmatrix} 2 \\ 3 \end{pmatrix}$, $\vec{AD} = \begin{pmatrix} -1 \\ 7 \end{pmatrix}$.

Show the points on squared paper. Find $\vec{BC}$ and $\vec{CD}$. What follows for B, C and D?

11. In Fig. 3, $\vec{GF} = \mathbf{a}$, $\vec{DE} = 2\mathbf{a}$, $\vec{DG} = \mathbf{b}$, DH = 2 HF. Express in terms of $\mathbf{a}$ and $\mathbf{b}$, $\vec{DF}$, $\vec{HF}$, $\vec{GH}$, $\vec{HD}$ and $\vec{HE}$. Using the expressions for $\vec{GH}$ and $\vec{HE}$, what follows for G, H and E?

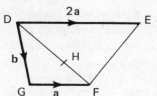

Fig. 3

12. $\mathbf{p} = 4\mathbf{i} + 3\mathbf{j}$ and $\mathbf{q} = 3\mathbf{i} + 4\mathbf{j}$. State the magnitude of $\mathbf{p}$. Express $\mathbf{p} + \mathbf{q}$ and $\mathbf{p} - \mathbf{q}$ in terms of $\mathbf{i}$ and $\mathbf{j}$. State the angle between them.

13. OPQRST is a regular hexagon. $\vec{OP} = \mathbf{a}$ and $\vec{OT} = \mathbf{b}$. Express in terms of $\mathbf{a}$ and $\mathbf{b}$, $\vec{QR}$, $\vec{SR}$, $\vec{TQ}$, $\vec{OQ}$, $\vec{OR}$ and $\vec{OS}$.

14. $\vec{OA} = 2\mathbf{x}$, $\vec{OB} = 2\mathbf{y}$, $\vec{OC} = -\mathbf{x}$ and $\vec{OD} = -\mathbf{y}$. Show the points O, A, B, C and D in a figure. Express in terms of $\mathbf{x}$ and $\mathbf{y}$, $\vec{AB}$, $\vec{BC}$, $\vec{CD}$ and $\vec{DA}$. Which are parallel? Show that $\vec{AB} + \vec{BC} + \vec{CD} + \vec{DA} = 0$.

15. $\mathbf{a} = \begin{pmatrix} 2 \\ 5 \end{pmatrix}$, $\mathbf{b} = \begin{pmatrix} -1 \\ 4 \end{pmatrix}$, $\mathbf{c} = \begin{pmatrix} 8 \\ 7 \end{pmatrix}$. Find x and y such that $x\mathbf{a} + y\mathbf{b} = \mathbf{c}$. Find k such that $\begin{pmatrix} 5 \\ k \end{pmatrix}$ is perpendicular to $\mathbf{a}$.

16. With origin 0, mark A (5, 7), B (11, 3) and C (10, 9).

(a) If $\vec{OD} = \vec{OA} + \vec{OB}$, write $\vec{OD}$ as a column vector. Also write $\vec{OM}$ as a column vector if $\vec{OM} = \frac{1}{2}\vec{OD}$.

(b) If $\vec{OE} = \vec{OA} + \vec{OB} - \vec{OC}$, write $\vec{OE}$ as a column vector.

(c) Show M and E in your figure and comment on C, M and E. Check by expressing $\vec{EM}$ and $\vec{MC}$ as column vectors.

Geometric transformations

Exercise 56

Illustrate each of the questions **1–4** with a diagram, labelling clearly the original points and their images:

1. State the coordinates of the points (3, 4), (3, −4) and (−3, −4) after a translation of (a) 2 units in the positive x direction (b) 3 units in the positive y direction (c) 2 units in the positive x direction followed by 3 units in the positive y direction.

State each of the translations as a column vector.

2. State the coordinates of the image of $(5, 2)$ after reflection (a) in the x-axis (b) in the y-axis (c) in the line $y = x$ (d) in the line $y = -x$ (e) in the line $x = 3$ (f) in the line $y = -1$.

3. Mark A as $(5, 2)$ and join OA. State the image of A after an anticlockwise rotation about O through (a) $90°$ (b) $180°$ (c) $270°$ (d) $360°$.

4. Find the image of $(5, 2)$ after an anticlockwise rotation of $90°$ about (a) $(5, 0)$ (b) $(1, 2)$ (c) $(1, 0)$ (d) $(3, 3)$.

   For questions 5–7 use triangle ABC where A is $(1, 1)$, B is $(2, 1)$ and C is $(1, 3)$.

5. Draw $\triangle ABC$. Mark as A_1, B_1, C_1 the images of A, B, C after reflection in the x-axis and as A_2, B_2, C_2 the images of A, B, C after reflection in the y-axis.

6. Draw $\triangle ABC$ and its image $A'\,B'\,C'$ after a clockwise rotation of $90°$ about O.

7. Draw $\triangle ABC$ and (a) its image $\triangle A_1 B_1 C_1$ after enlargement with centre O and scale factor 3 (b) its image $\triangle A_2 B_2 C_2$ after enlargement with centre O and scale factor $\frac{1}{2}$ (c) its image $\triangle A_3 B_3 C_3$ after enlargement with centre O and scale factor $-\frac{3}{2}$.

8. (a) A rotation about O maps $(4, -1)$ onto $(1, 4)$. Find the image of $(-2, -3)$.
   (b) A reflection maps $(4, 5)$ onto $(4, 1)$. State the axis of reflection and the image of $(5, 6)$.

9. $A(x, y)$ is the image of (x, y) after reflection in the x-axis. $D(x, y)$ is the image of (x, y) after rotation through $90°$ anticlockwise about O. DA means 'do A first and then D'. Show in a diagram $(1, 4)$, $A(1, 4)$, DA$(1, 4)$, D$(1, 4)$, AD$(1, 4)$. Is DA = AD?

10. (a) Draw $\triangle ABC$ as in questions 5 to 7. Draw the reflection of $\triangle ABC$ in the y-axis and label it F. Draw the image of F after an anticlockwise rotation through $90°$ about O and label it G.
    (b) On a separate diagram draw $\triangle ABC$ again. Draw its image after an anticlockwise rotation through $90°$ about O and label it H. Draw the reflection of H in the y-axis and label it J. Is J the same as G?

Matrices and transformations

The matrix $\begin{pmatrix} 3 & -1 \\ 0 & 2 \end{pmatrix}$ transforms P $(4, 5)$ onto P′. To find the coordinates of P′ we pre-multiply the column vector $\begin{pmatrix} 4 \\ 5 \end{pmatrix}$ by the 2×2 matrix.

$\begin{pmatrix} 3 & -1 \\ 0 & 2 \end{pmatrix} \begin{pmatrix} 4 \\ 5 \end{pmatrix} = \begin{pmatrix} 7 \\ 10 \end{pmatrix}$. P′ is $(7, 10)$.

Exercise 57

Take $A = \begin{pmatrix} 1 & 0 \\ 0 & -1 \end{pmatrix}$, $B = \begin{pmatrix} -1 & 0 \\ 0 & 1 \end{pmatrix}$, $C = \begin{pmatrix} 0 & 1 \\ 1 & 0 \end{pmatrix}$

$D = \begin{pmatrix} 0 & -1 \\ 1 & 0 \end{pmatrix}$, $E = \begin{pmatrix} 0 & 1 \\ -1 & 0 \end{pmatrix}$, $F = \begin{pmatrix} 0 & -1 \\ -1 & 0 \end{pmatrix}$

1. Apply the matrix $\begin{pmatrix} 0 & 3 \\ 1 & 2 \end{pmatrix}$ to the points $(1, 4)$ and $(-2, 3)$.

2. Apply the matrix $\begin{pmatrix} -1 & 2 \\ 0 & -2 \end{pmatrix}$ to the points $(-5, 2)$ and $(4, -4)$.

3. Join $(1, 2)$ to $(1, 4)$ and join $(1, 4)$ to $(2, 4)$. Apply matrix A to the figure and show its new position. Describe the transformation geometrically. Repeat using each of the matrices B, C, D, E, and F.

4. Draw again the figure of question 3 and label it I. Apply D to I and label it II. Apply A to II and label it III? Which single matrix produces this transformation? Show that AD is equal to this matrix.

5. Draw again the figure of question 3. Show that applying B and then C produces the same result as applying E. Verify that CB = E.

6. (a) Join the points $(1, 1)$, $(2, 1)$ and $(1, 3)$ to form a triangle. Apply the matrix $\begin{pmatrix} 2 & 0 \\ 0 & 2 \end{pmatrix}$ to the triangle and draw its image. Describe the result geometrically.

   (b) Repeat (a) using $\begin{pmatrix} -\frac{1}{2} & 0 \\ 0 & -\frac{1}{2} \end{pmatrix}$.

7. Plot $P(1, 1)$, $Q(2, 1)$, $R(2, 2)$, $S(1, 2)$ and join them to form a square. Apply $\begin{pmatrix} 3 & 0 \\ 0 & 1 \end{pmatrix}$ to the square and show its image as $P'Q'R'S'$. Which sides of the square have not changed in length? How has the length of PQ changed? The transformation is a **stretch** in the x direction.

8. (a) Join the points $O(0, 0)$, $A(2, 0)$, $B(2, 2)$ and $C(0, 2)$ to form a square. Apply $\begin{pmatrix} 1 & 2 \\ 0 & 1 \end{pmatrix}$ to the square and show its image as $OA'B'C'$. Notice that it is a parallelogram. The transformation is a **shear** in the x direction.

   (b) Draw the square OABC again and apply the matrix $\begin{pmatrix} 1 & 0 \\ 3 & 1 \end{pmatrix}$. Describe the transformation.

9. Find the 2 × 2 matrix which transforms $(1, 0)$ to $(5, 2)$ and $(0, 1)$ to $(3, 4)$. Find the images of $(2, -1)$ and $(-1, 3)$ under this transformation.

10. Apply the matrix $M = \begin{pmatrix} 2 & -1 \\ -1 & 1 \end{pmatrix}$ to the square of question 8. Show the the original square OABC and its image $OA_1 B_1 C_1$ in a figure. State the inverse of M. Verify that this inverse transforms $OA_1 B_1 C_1$ back to OABC.

11. Join $O(0, 0)$, $P(2, 0)$, $Q(2, 1)$ and $R(0, 1)$ to form a rectangle. Apply the matrix $G = \begin{pmatrix} 0.8 & -0.6 \\ 0.6 & 0.8 \end{pmatrix}$ and show the image as $OP_1 Q_1 R_1$. Measure $P\hat{O}P_1$ and describe the transformation.

Form the product HG where $H = \begin{pmatrix} 0.6 & -0.8 \\ 0.8 & 0.6 \end{pmatrix}$. Apply HG to the original rectangle OPQR and show its image as $OP_2 Q_2 R_2$. Describe the transformation. Hence state the transformation corresponding to H.

Sine, cosine and tangent

Acute angles

$$\sin \theta = \frac{\text{opposite side}}{\text{hypotenuse}}$$

$$\cos \theta = \frac{\text{adjacent side}}{\text{hypotenuse}}$$

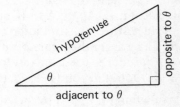

Fig. 1

$$\tan \theta = \frac{\text{opposite side}}{\text{adjacent side}}$$

If AB = 8 cm and $B\hat{A}C = 70°$

$\dfrac{BC}{AB} = \tan A$, $\dfrac{BC}{8} = \tan 70° \simeq 2.7475$

BC $\simeq 8 \times 2.7475 = 21.98$

$\qquad\qquad = 22.0$ to 3 sig. fig.

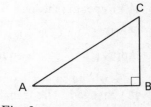

Fig. 2

If BC = 6.8 cm and AC = 9.2 cm

$\sin A = \dfrac{BC}{AC} = \dfrac{6.8}{9.2} \simeq 0.7391$

$A \simeq 47.7°$ or $47°39'$

Exercise 58

For questions **1** to **6**, use Fig. 2:
1. If AB = 9 cm and $\hat{A} = 32°$, calculate BC.
2. If AB = 6 cm and BC = 9 cm, calculate $\hat{A}$.
3. If AC = 10 cm and $\hat{A} = 53°$, calculate BC.
4. If AC = 8 cm and $\hat{A} = 60°$, calculate AB.
5. If AC = 10 cm and AB = 7.3 cm, calculate $\hat{A}$.
6. If AC = 5.8 cm and BC = 2.6 cm, calculate $\hat{A}$.

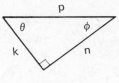

Fig. 3

7. In Fig. 3, $\tan \theta = n/k$. State, in this way, $\sin \theta$ and $\cos \theta$.
8. In Fig. 3, state fractions equal to $\tan \phi$, $\sin \phi$ and $\cos \phi$.
9. Using Fig. 3, if $\sin \theta = \frac{3}{5}$, state $\tan \theta$ and $\cos \theta$ in fraction form.
10. In Fig. 3, if $k = 7$ cm and $\theta = 68°$, calculate n.
11. In Fig. 3, if $p = 40$ cm and $\phi = 29°$, calculate k.
12. In Fig. 3, if $n = 30$ cm and $\theta = 35°$, calculate ϕ and k.
13. From a point 33 m from a tower, the angle of elevation of the top is 28°. Calculate the height of the tower.
14. From the top of a vertical cliff 90 m high, the angle of depression of a boat is 32°. Calculate the distance of the boat from the foot of the cliff.
15. (a) P is (7, 4) and O is (0, 0). Calculate the angle between OP and the x-axis.
    (b) OQ is 10 units long and at 18° to the x-axis. Calculate the co-ordinates of Q, correct to 3 sig. fig.
16. A vertical post of height 6.4 m has a shadow of length 8.3 m on horizontal ground. What is the angle of elevation of the sun?
17. A boat sails for 8 km on a course of 156°. How far east is it of its starting point?
18. A ladder of length 6 m has one end against a vertical wall and the other on horizontal ground. If the ladder is at 70° to the ground, how far up the wall does it reach?

Finding a hypotenuse

$\dfrac{8}{h} = \cos 28° \simeq 0.8829$, $\dfrac{h}{8} = \dfrac{1}{0.8829} \simeq 1.1326$

$h = 8 \times 1.1326 = 9.0608 = 9.06$ to 3 sig. fig.

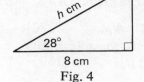

Fig. 4

Using an isosceles triangle
PN divides $\triangle PQR$ into two congruent right-angled triangles.

$\dfrac{x}{6} = \cos 75° \simeq 0.2588$

$x = 6 \times 0.2588 = 1.5528$
$2x = 3.1056$, QR = 3.11 to 3 sig. fig.

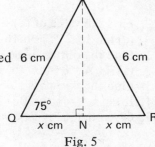

Fig. 5

71

Exercise 59

1. In Fig. 2, if AB = 10 cm and $\hat{A}$ = 24°, calculate AC.
2. In Fig. 2, if BC = 7 cm and $\hat{A}$ = 38°, calculate AC.
3. In Fig. 3, if k = 8 cm and ϕ = 70°, calculate p.
4. In Fig. 5, calculate PN.
5. An isosceles triangle has sides of 10 cm and base angles of 80°. Calculate the length of the base and the height of the triangle.
6. An isosceles triangle has sides of 9 cm, 12 cm and 12 cm. Calculate its angles.
7. A rectangle has sides of 10 cm and 12 cm. Calculate the acute angle between the diagonals.
8. The four corners of a regular pentagon ABCDE lie on a circle of radius 8 cm and centre O. Calculate (a) A$\hat{O}$B (b) side AB.
9. A rhombus has sides of 15 cm and two angles of 140°. Calculate the length of the diagonals.

Obtuse angles

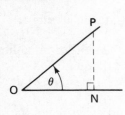

Fig. 6

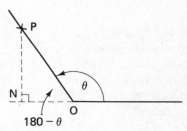

Fig. 7

We can define $\sin \theta$ as $\dfrac{PN}{OP}$, $\cos \theta$ as $\dfrac{ON}{OP}$ and $\tan \theta$ as $\dfrac{PN}{ON}$.

When θ is obtuse, ON is negative and so $\cos \theta$ and $\tan \theta$ are negative. Hence when θ is obtuse, $\sin \theta = \sin (180 - \theta)$, $\cos \theta = -\cos (180 - \theta)$ and $\tan = -\tan (180 - \theta)$.

Exercise 60

1. Find the value of (a) sin 130° (b) cos 135° (c) tan 110° (d) cos 108° (e) tan 152° (f) sin 164.5° (g) tan 128.7° (h) cos 99.3°.
2. Find the obtuse angle in the following cases:
   (a) sin A = 0.9063 (b) cos B = −0.9613 (c) tan C = −1.5399
3. Find the two possible values of D if sin D = 0.9659 and 0° < D < 180°
4. If $\tan x = -\frac{3}{4}$ and 0° < x < 180°, state as fractions sin x and cos x.
5. Given that 0° < θ < 180°, find θ if
   (a) tan θ = −1.4826   (b) cos θ = 0.9272   (c) sin θ = 0.3090
   (d) cos θ = −0.6691   (e) sin θ = 0.6947   (f) tan θ = 0.5095

6. (a) R is $(-8, 5)$, W is $(7, 0)$ and O is $(0, 0)$. Find tan WÔR and hence WÔR.

(b) OT = 8 units and WÔT = 115°. Calculate the coordinates of T to 3 sig. fig.

Angle properties of circles

Exercise 61

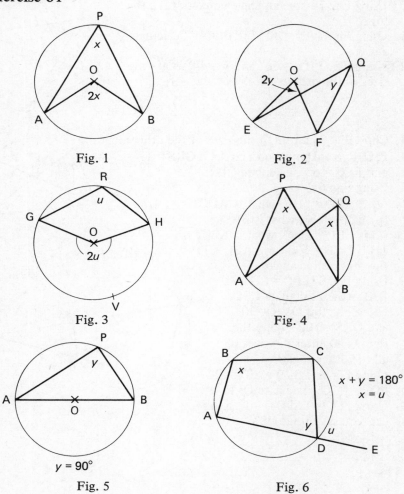

Fig. 1

Fig. 2

Fig. 3

Fig. 4

$y = 90°$

Fig. 5

$x + y = 180°$
$x = u$

Fig. 6

1. Using Fig. 1 (a) if AP̂B = 42°, state AÔB. (b) if AÔB = 116°, state AP̂B.
2. Using Fig. 2 (a) if EQ̂F = 54°, state EÔF. (b) if EÔF = 166°, state EQF.
3. Using Fig. 3 (a) if GR̂H = 125°, state reflex angle GOH. (b) if reflex angle GOH = 224°, state GR̂H.
4. Using Fig. 3 if obtuse angle GOH = 100°, calculate GR̂H.
5. Copy Fig. 3 and join GV and HV. If GV̂H = 80° and RĜO = 60°, calculate both the angles at O, GR̂H and RĤO.
6. Copy Fig. 1 and join PO. If PÂO = 20° and PB̂O = 35°, calculate AÔB, AÔP and BÔP.
7. In Fig. 3, if reflex angle GOH = 220° and GR is parallel to OH, calculate all the angles of quadrilateral GRHO.
8. In Fig. 3, if OGRH is a parallelogram, calculate GR̂H.
9. CD is the diameter of a circle, centre O. K is a point on the circumference. State the size of CK̂D. If KĈD = 37°, calculate KD̂C.
10. Using Fig. 7 name an angle equal to (a) a (b) b (c) c
11. Using Fig. 7 if f = 40° and d = 95°, calculate g and b.
12. Using Fig. 7 if a = 66° and b = 44°, state the sizes of the other angles.

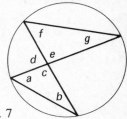

Fig. 7

13. Copy Fig. 8 and fill in the sizes of the other angles.
14. P, Q, R, S are points on a circle. If QR̂S = 80° and RQ̂S = 65°, calculate QP̂R.
15. Using Fig. 6
    (a) if ABC = 110°, what is AD̂C?
    (b) BĈD = 68°, what is BÂD?
    (c) If ED̂C = 100°, what is AB̂C?
    (d) If DĈB = 130° and AB̂C = 115°, calculate the other three angles.

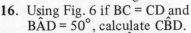

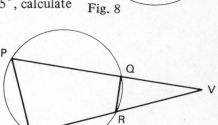

Fig. 8

16. Using Fig. 6 if BC = CD and BÂD = 50°, calculate CB̂D.
17. Using Fig. 9 if QV̂R = 30° and QR̂S = 100°, copy the figure and enter the sizes of all the other angles.
18. Using Fig. 9 if SP̂Q = 80° and PQ̂R = 110°, calculate QV̂R.
19. Using Fig. 9 if SP̂Q = 90°, what can you say about QS?

Fig. 9

20. Chord PQ of a circle is parallel to diameter AB.
    (a) If PB̂A = 35°, calculate PÂB, PQ̂B, QP̂B and PB̂Q.
    (b) If PB̂A = $x°$, express PB̂Q in terms of x.

Chords of circles

If OH is perpendicular to AB, then AH = HB.
Conversely, if AH = HB, then OH is perpendicular to AB.

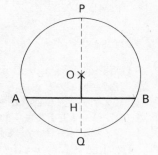

Fig. 1

Exercise 62

Use Figure 1 with OH perpendicular to AB for questions **1** to **5**:
1. If OH = 6 cm and AB = 16 cm, calculate OA.
2. If AO = 17 cm and OH = 8 cm, calculate AB.
3. If AÔB = 110° and AO = 9 cm, calculate AÔH, OÂB, OH and HQ.
4. If AO = 10 cm and AB = 13 cm, calculate AÔB.
5. If PH = 8 cm and HQ = 2 cm, state the lengths of PQ, OQ, OA and OH. Also calculate AB.
6. Two circles of radii 17 cm and 10 cm have the same centre, O. A straight line ACDB meets the larger circle at A and B and the smaller circle at C and D. N is the mid-point of chord CD and ON = 8 cm. Calculate ND, NB and AB.
7. Construct a triangle PQR having PQ = 7 cm, QR = 6 cm and RP = 5 cm. Construct the mediator (perpendicular bisector) of PQ and the mediator of QR. Let them meet at C. With centre C and radius CP, draw a circle. It should pass through Q and R. Explain why. It is the circumcircle of the triangle. Measure its radius.

Intersecting chords

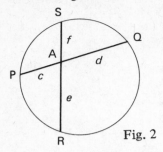

Fig. 2

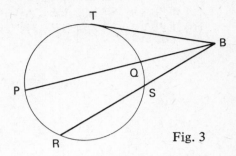

Fig. 3

In Fig. 2 chords PQ and RS, intersect at A. AP × AQ = AR × AS. In Fig. 3 chords PQ and RS are produced to meet at B and BT is a tangent.
$BP \times BQ = BR \times BS = BT^2$

Exercise 63

Use Fig. 2 for questions **1** to **4**:
1. If $c = 4$, $d = 9$ and $f = 3$, calculate e.
2. If $f = 3$, $e = 6$ and $d = 4$, calculate c.
3. If PQ = 13, PA = 7 and SA = 5, calculate SR.
4. If $f = 4$, $e = 9$ and A is the mid-point of PQ, calculate PQ.
   Use Fig. 3 for questions **5** to **8**:
5. If PQ = 7, BQ = 3 and BS = 5, calculate BR and RS.
6. If BQ = 2 and PQ = 6, calculate BT.
7. If BT = 6 and BS = 4, calculate RS.
8. If BQ = 7 and PQ = 5, calculate BT, correct to 2 sig. fig.
   Use Fig. 4 in which O is the centre DE is a diameter and FG is a chord for questions **9** to **11**:

Fig. 4

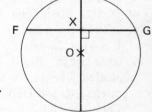

9. If DX = 2 and the radius is 5, calculate FG.
10. If DX = 8 and FG = 24, calculate the radius.
11. If FG = 16 and the radius is 10, calculate DX.
    (*Hint*: Let DX = y and express XE in terms of y.)
12. Water is poured into a spherical bowl with a hole at the top. The radius of the bowl is 10 cm and the surface of the water is a circle of radius 6 cm. If the bowl is over half full, calculate the depth of the water. (Use Fig. 4.)
13. An arch of a bridge has the form of an arc of a circle, such as FDG in Fig. 4. If the width of the arch (FG) is 20 m and the greatest height (XD) is 4 m, calculate the radius of the arch.

Tangents to circles

Exercise 64

For questions **1** to **9**, use Fig. 1 in which TK is a tangent, TNO is a straight line and O is the centre of the circle. It follows that $T\hat{K}O = 90°$:

1. If $T\hat{O}K = 65°$, calculate $K\hat{T}O$.
2. If $K\hat{T}O = 20°$, calculate $K\hat{O}T$, $O\hat{N}K$ and $N\hat{K}T$.
3. If $O\hat{K}N = 65°$, calculate $K\hat{T}O$.
4. If KN = NT and $N\hat{K}T = x°$, express $K\hat{N}O$ and $O\hat{K}N$ in terms of x. Hence calculate x and comment on △OKN.

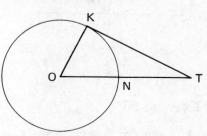

Fig. 1

5. If OK = 6 cm and OT = 10 cm, calculate KT and $K\hat{O}T$.
6. If OK = 5 cm and KT = 12 cm, calculate OT and $K\hat{O}T$.
7. If ON = 8 cm and NT = 9 cm, calculate TK.
8. If OK = 7 cm and OT = 13 cm, calculate KT, correct to 1 d. p.
9. If OK = 5 cm and $K\hat{O}T = 72°$, calculate KT, correct to 3 sig. fig.

For questions **10** to **13** use Fig. 2 in which PA and PB are tangents, O is the centre of the circle and ADB and ODP are straight lines:

10. Name the line of symmetry of the figure. State the size of $A\hat{D}P$. Name a line or angle equal to each of the following: (a) AP (b) $A\hat{P}D$ (c) $A\hat{O}D$ (d) $D\hat{A}P$ (e) AD. What kind of quadrilateral is PAOB?

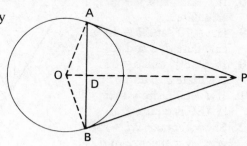

Fig. 2

11. If $A\hat{P}B = 36°$, calculate $D\hat{A}P$ and $A\hat{O}D$.
12. State the sum of the angles of quadrilateral OAPB. If $A\hat{P}B = 44°$, calculate $A\hat{O}B$.
13. If AP = 12 cm and $A\hat{P}B = 50°$, calculate AB.

Alternate segment property

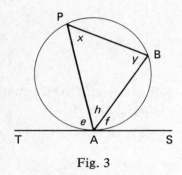

Fig. 3

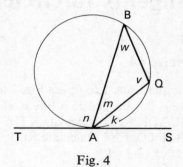

Fig. 4

Exercise 65

1. Using fig. 3 name an angle equal to x. If $e = 72°$ and $h = 50°$, calculate x.
2. Using Fig. 3 if $h = 85°$ and $x = 50°$, calculate e.
3. Using Fig. 3 if PB = BA and $y = 52°$, calculate f.
4. Using Fig. 4 name an angle equal to v. If $k = 25°$ and $m = 45°$, calculate v.
5. Using Fig. 4 if $n = 130°$ and AQ = BQ, calculate k.
  Use Fig. 5 for questions **6** to **12**:
6. Name two angles equal to d. If $d = 72°$, calculate x and a.
7. If $a = 66°$, calculate x and d.
8. If $f = 35°$ and $y = 70°$, calculate x.
9. If $a = 70°$ and $b = 46°$, calculate d, e and f.
10. If $d = 80°$ and $e = 62°$, calculate a, b and c.
11. If $d = 60°$, show that $\triangle$ AEF is equilateral.
12. Show that $a + 2d = 180°$, whatever the size of d.

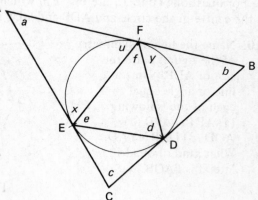

Fig. 5

78

Loci

A locus is a set of points which satisfy a given condition. Sometimes we think of a locus as the path of a point moving in such a way that it satisfies a given condition. The shape of a locus can often be found by marking several points which satisfy the condition.

Exercise 66

1. In each of the following cases, make a sketch to show several points satisfying the condition and then indicate the locus with a suitable straight line or curve and describe its nature.
   (a) Points 2 cm from a given point.
   (b) Points 1 cm from a given straight line, assumed to continue indefinitely in each direction.
   (c) Points which are equidistant from two given points C and D. (For any point P on the locus, PC = PD.)
   (d) Points which are 1 cm from a line segment of length 5 cm. (This consist of two line segments and two curves.)
   (e) Points which are equidistant from two straight lines, COD and EOF, assumed to continue indefinitely in each direction.
   (f) Points which are equidistant from two fixed parallel straight lines.
2. On graph paper draw the locus of points which are (a) 5 units from O (b) 3 units from the y-axis. Label, as A and B, the two points which are on both loci.
3. Describe the locus in space for each of the following:
   (a) Points 10 cm from a fixed point.
   (b) Points 10 cm from a fixed line, assumed infinite.
   (c) Points equidistant from two points.
4. QR is a fixed line segment of length 6 cm and P is a movable point. For each of the following cases, sketch the locus and describe it in words: (a) the area of $\triangle$QPR is 15 cm^2 (b) $Q\hat{P}R = 90°$.
5. Mark two points, C and D, 5 cm apart. Draw the loci: (a) $\{K : CK = DK\}$ (b) $\{L : CL = CD\}$ (c) $\{M : DM = CD\}$. Mark as P and Q the two points common to all three sets and measure $C\hat{P}D$.
6. Mark two points, A and B, 7 cm apart. Draw the loci (a) $\{P : A\hat{P}B = 90°\}$ (b) $\{Q : A\hat{B}Q = 90°\}$ (c) $\{R : B\hat{A}R = 90°\}$. Show, by shading, the locus $\{T : $ each angle of $\triangle TAB$ is acute$\}$.

Graphs of data

In a **pie chart** each quantity is represented by the area of a sector of a circle and hence by an angle at the centre of the circle.
In a **bar chart** the **length** of each bar represents a quantity.
In a **histogram** the **area** of each rectangle represents a quantity.

Exercise 67

1. The pie chart shows how a boy spent the 24 hours of a certain day. What angle represents one hour? State the time spent (a) watching TV (b) asleep (c) at school (d) playing soccer. Suggest how some of the remaining time might have been spent.

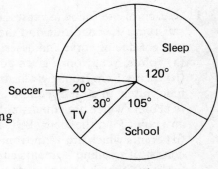

Fig. 1

2. Out of 120 pupils who left a school one term, 30 started work in factories, 20 in offices and 10 in shops, 40 had places in universities and colleges and 5 were going to other schools. How many does this leave out of the 120? Draw a pie chart to represent the data.

3. On a certain day, the hours of sunshine at five resorts were: Dunbar 3, Douglas 6, Swanage 8, Jersey 11, Clacton 4. Draw a bar chart to illustrate the data.

4. A pupil counted the cars of various colours on a car park and drew a bar chart for the results. He used bars of the following heights: red 55 mm, blue 45 mm, brown or yellow 90 mm, grey or green 65 mm, white 35 mm. There were 7 white cars. How many were there of each of the other colours?

5. The number of seeds per pod for a sample of 50 pods were:
   6, 8, 7, 4, 6, 5, 6, 4, 4, 8, 5, 6, 9, 6, 6, 5, 8, 5, 5, 4
   7, 5, 8, 8, 7, 9, 5, 4, 4, 6, 5, 5, 6, 8, 8, 7, 4, 6, 4, 8
   9, 5, 3, 5, 4, 5, 7, 7, 6, 2.
   Draw up a tally chart and a frequency table. Construct a bar chart and state the most frequent number of seeds (the mode).

6. 30 pupils were asked to state the time for their journey to school.

80

Fig. 2 is a histogram for the results. Each square represents 2 pupils. The left rectangle represents 8 pupils who took up to 5 minutes to get to school. How many pupils took (a) between 5 and 10 min (b) 10 to 20 min (c) 20 to 40 min?

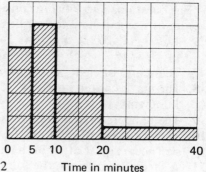

Fig. 2   Time in minutes

7. The table shows the ages of taxis owned by a certain taxi firm.

Age in years	0-1	1-3	3-5	5-9
Number of taxis	20	24	16	8

Draw a histogram using 1 square to represent 4 taxis.

8. The following marks were obtained by 30 pupils in an examination.

3, 9, 11, 13, 16, 17, 17, 19, 21, 22, 23, 23, 23, 25, 25, 25, 27, 28, 30, 32, 33, 33, 33, 36, 36, 37, 40, 40, 42, 42

Draw up a table showing the number of pupils in each of the ranges 0-9, 10-19, 20-29, 30-39, 40-49 and draw a histogram.

Mean, median and mode

Exercise 68

1. (a) A pupil's marks in nine tests were 14, 17, 11, 12, 11, 18, 15, 9, 12. Add up the marks and divide by 9, giving your answer correct to 1 d.p. This is the **mean** of the marks. (b) If the mark of 9 had been 2, what would the mean have been? This shows how much the mean is affected by an exceptionally low (or high) value.
2. (a) List the marks of question **1** (a) in order of size and state the middle mark. This is the **median** mark.
(b) For an even number of values, the median is taken as the mean of the middle two values. If the pupil scored 19 in the next test, find the median mark for the ten tests.

For questions **3** to **9** (a) Arrange the numbers or measurements in order of size and state the median (b) Calculate the mean:

3. 4, 9, 3, 11, 10, 11, 8   **4.** 14, 6, 10, 14, 13, 4, 18

5. 11, 7, 3, 13,   **6.** 10, 12, 38, 35, 23, 14

7. The scores of eight people playing darts: 23, 40, 8, 158, 25, 10, 4, 36

8. The masses of ten pupils: 47, 55, 49, 50, 51, 50, 45, 53, 47, 42 kilograms

9. The temperatures at noon on six days: $-7, -5, -2, 3, 0, -4\,°C$

10. The shoe sizes of eight pupils were: $6, 6\frac{1}{2}, 6\frac{1}{2}, 7, 7, 7, 7, 7\frac{1}{2}$. What size occurs most often in the list? This is the **mode**.

11. A soccer team scored the following number of goals in ten matches: 0, 2, 1, 3, 0, 1, 2, 5, 2, 2. Find (a) the mode (b) the median (c) the mean.

12. The heights in centimetres of seven men are: 177, 161, 180, 169, 166, 185, 174. The calculation of the mean is simplified by using 170 as working origin. The heights exceed 170 cm by $7, -9, 10, -1, -4, 15, 4$ cm. Find the mean of these excesses, correct to 1 d.p. and add it to 170 cm to obtain the mean of the original heights.

13. The ages at which eight men retired were: 64, 62, 61, 67, 65, 66, 65. Using a working origin of 60, calculate the mean.

14. The barometer readings at noon each day for a week were: 1006, 1002, 980, 972, 1008, 1012, 1010 millibars. Find the mean, correct to 0.1 millibar.

15. The heights of eight boys were 163, 147, 157, 170, 158, 155, 143, 148 cm and the heights of six girls were 142, 134, 140, 136, 145, 162 cm. Compare the two sets by finding their means.

16. A cricketer has a mean of 22 runs per innings over 10 innings. In the next two innings he scores 6 and 14. What is his new mean?

17. The ages of the members of a family are 43, 39, 18, 16 and 14. Find the mean age. From this, write down the mean age (a) 4 years ago (b) in 4 years time.

18. In four tests a girl scored 8, 3, 6 and 5 marks. Find her mean score. What must she score in the next test to raise her mean to 6?

19. In an examination, the mean mark for a class of 30 pupils was 52 and the mean for a second class of 26 pupils was 65. Calculate correct to the nearest unit, the mean for the group of 56 pupils.

Means of frequency distributions

One Saturday afternoon, the number of goals scored by fifty teams were as follows: 9 teams scored 0, 21 scored 1, 12 scored 2, 5 scored 3 and 3 scored 4.

The mean number of goals per team is calculated thus:

Goals x	Frequency f	xf
0	9	0
1	21	21
2	12	24
3	5	15
4	3	12
Total	50	72

The 12 teams scoring 2 each contributed 24 goals to the total, the 5 teams scoring 3 each contributed 15, etc.

$$\text{Mean} = \frac{\text{total number of goals}}{\text{total number of teams}} = \frac{72}{50}$$
$$= 1.4 \text{ approximately}$$

In general, $\quad \text{mean} = \dfrac{\text{sum of (frequency} \times \text{value)}}{\text{sum of frequencies}} = \dfrac{\Sigma fx}{\Sigma f}$

If a working origin of w is used and d is a deviation from it,

$$\text{mean} = w + \frac{\Sigma fd}{\Sigma f}$$

Exercise 69

1. Find the mean of the following frequency distributions:

   (a) x 1 2 3 4 5
   $\quad\ \ f$ 3 6 10 14 7

   (b) x 0 1 2 3 4 5
   $\quad\ \ f$ 5 8 9 5 2 1

2. Calculate the mean number of peas per pod from the following:

Number of peas per pod (x)	4	5	6	7	8
Number of pods (f)	4	14	18	11	3

3. Using suitable working origins, find the means of

   (a) x 41 42 43 44
   $\quad\ \ f$ 8 12 14 6

   (b) x 298 299 300 301 302 303
   $\quad\ \ f$ 6 2 7 4 13 8

4. The masses of forty packets of chocolate marked 50 g were measured and this table compiled:

Mass	48	49	50	51	52	53
Frequency	1	5	16	12	4	2

   Calculate the mean mass, using a working origin of 50

5. For each of the following, state the centres of the intervals and calculate the mean:

(a)
x	1-5	6-10	11-15	16-20	21-25
f	4	7	5	2	2

(b)
x	16.0-16.4	16.5-16.9	17.0-17.4	17.5-17.9
f	13	31	47	9

6. The table shows the masses of 80 pupils measured to the nearest kg:

Mass (kg)	40-43	44-47	48-51	52-55	56-59	60-63	64-67
Frequency	2	7	14	23	18	12	4

The first interval, 40-43 kg, can be represented by the centre of the interval, $41\frac{1}{2}$ kg. Use a working origin of $53\frac{1}{2}$ kg, calculate the mean.

7. The estimates of fifty pupils for the length of a line to the nearest centimetre were as follows:

Length (cm)	9	10	11	12	13	14	15
Frequency	2	5	9	13	12	8	1

(a) State the modal estimate.
(b) Calculate the mean estimate.
(c) The true length was 13 cm. What percentage of the estimates were too large?

Probability

If a trial has n equally likely outcomes and a certain event can happen in x of these outcomes, then the probability of the event is x/n. When drawing a card from a pack of playing cards, there are 52 possible outcomes. A heart can occur in 13 ways. Therefore $p(\text{heart}) = \frac{13}{52} = \frac{1}{4}$.

If an event is certain to happen, its probability is 1: if an event is impossible, its probability is 0.

If the probability of an event occurring is p, then the probability of it not occurring is $1 - p$. $p(\text{not a heart}) = 1 - \frac{1}{4} = \frac{3}{4}$.

Expected Number of Successes: When a card is drawn from a pack, p (heart) $= \frac{1}{4}$. If a card is drawn 100 times (with replacement and shuffling) the expected number of times a heart is obtained is $\frac{1}{4}$ of 100 = 25. (In practice it is very unlikely to be exactly 25 but is likely to be between 20 and 30).

Exercise 70

1. A die is thrown. What is the probability of (a) a six (b) a five or a six (c) an even number (d) a seven?
2. A card is drawn from a pack of 52 playing cards. What is the probability of (a) a diamond (b) a king (c) the king of diamonds (d) a red card (e) a king, queen or jack?
3. Nine counters having the integers 1 to 9 are placed in a box. One counter is drawn out. State the probability that it has (a) an odd number (b) an even number (c) 8 or 9 (d) less than 4.
4. A letter is chosen at random from the word DIAMOND. What is the probability that it is (a) a D (b) a vowel (c) not a vowel (d) a T?
5. A drawer contains ten red ties, six white ones and four blue ones. One tie is taken out at random. Find the probability that it is (a) red (b) white (c) not white (d) red or blue (e) green.
6. A die is thrown sixty times. How many times would you expect (a) a six (b) an odd number (c) five or six?
7. A car park contains sixty cars. How many would you expect to have a registration number ending in (a) 3 (b) 0, 1 or 2?
8. A number is chosen at random from {11, 12, 13, . . . 40}. What is the probability that (a) the first digit is 3 (b) the second digit is 3 (c) both digits are 3s (d) only one digit is 3?
9. Two dice are thrown and the numbers added together. Draw up a table showing how possible totals are obtained. What is the probability of a total of (a) 3 (b) 5 (c) 7 (d) more than 10.
10. Three dice are thrown together. Explain why there are 216 possible outcomes. Write down in the form 2 + 2 + 1 the ways in which a total of 5 can be obtained. What is the probability of this total?

Sum Rule: If events A and B are **mutually exclusive**, i.e. they cannot both happen at the same time, $p(A \text{ or } B) = p(A) + p(B)$.
Product Rule: If events C and D are **independant**, i.e. they do not affect each other, then $p(C \text{ and } D) = p(C) \times p(D)$.
Consider a box containing 3 red, 2 blue and 5 green counters. If one is drawn out, $p(\text{red}) = \frac{3}{10}$ and $p(\text{green}) = \frac{5}{10}$. $p(\text{red or green}) = p(\text{red}) + p(\text{green}) = \frac{3}{10} + \frac{5}{10} = \frac{8}{10} = \frac{4}{5}$ or 0.8.
If one counter is drawn out and replaced and then a second draw is made, $p(\text{a red first and a green second}) = p(\text{red}) \times p(\text{green}) = \frac{3}{10} \times \frac{5}{10} = \frac{15}{100} = \frac{3}{20}$ or 0.15.

A tree diagram

Consider a box with 4 red counters and 2 blue counters. One is drawn out and not replaced. Another is then drawn out.

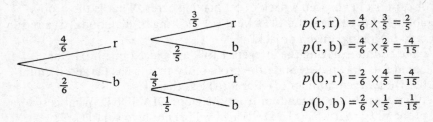

$$p(\text{r},\text{r}) = \tfrac{4}{6} \times \tfrac{3}{5} = \tfrac{2}{5}$$

$$p(\text{r},\text{b}) = \tfrac{4}{6} \times \tfrac{2}{5} = \tfrac{4}{15}$$

$$p(\text{b},\text{r}) = \tfrac{2}{6} \times \tfrac{4}{5} = \tfrac{4}{15}$$

$$p(\text{b},\text{b}) = \tfrac{2}{6} \times \tfrac{1}{5} = \tfrac{1}{15}$$

$p(\text{both the same colour}) = p(\text{r},\text{r}) + p(\text{b},\text{b}) = \tfrac{2}{5} + \tfrac{1}{15} = \tfrac{7}{15}.$

$p(\text{different colours}) = p(\text{r},\text{b}) + p(\text{b},\text{r}) = \tfrac{4}{15} + \tfrac{4}{15} = \tfrac{8}{15}.$

Exercise 71

1. The probability of A winning a certain race is $\tfrac{2}{5}$ and the probability of B winning it is $\tfrac{1}{4}$. Calculate the probability of either A or B winning.
2. The probability of a certain kind of seed germinating is $\tfrac{1}{10}$ and the probability of the plant flowering is $\tfrac{4}{5}$. Calculate the probability a seed germinates and the resulting plant flowers.
3. A die is thrown and a coin is spun. State (a) $p(\text{head})$, (b) $p(6)$ and (c) $p(\text{head and } 6)$.
4. A card is drawn from a pack of 52 playing cards. State (a) $p(\text{king})$ (b) $p(\text{number} > 6)$ (c) $p(\text{king or number} > 6)$.
5. (a) A coin is spun twice. Draw a probability tree. State the probability of (i) two heads (ii) two tails (iii) a tail followed by a head (iv) a tail and a head in either order.
   (b) A coin is spun three times. Draw a probability tree. State the probability of (i) two heads followed by a tail (ii) two heads and a tail in any order (iii) three heads.
6. Six cards are placed in a box. Two have crosses on them and the others are plain.
   (a) One is drawn out and replaced and then another is drawn out. Draw a tree. Find the probability of (i) two crosses (ii) one cross only (iii) no crosses. Check that these add up to 1.
   (b) One is drawn out and then a second without replacing the first. Draw another tree. Find the probabilities as in (a).
7. A bag has 3 red fruit drops and 7 green. One is taken out and eaten and then another is taken out. Draw a probability tree to show the possible outcomes. State the probability of (a) 2 red (b) one of each (c) 2 green. Check that they add up to 1.

8. I hold five playing cards—two hearts and three spades. Two cards are taken at random. What is the probability that they are (a) both hearts (b) both spades (c) one of each?
   Check that they add up to 1.

9. Three girls plan to meet one evening at a youth club. The probability that Joan is unable to go is $\frac{1}{3}$, the probability that Jane is unable to go is $\frac{1}{4}$ and the probability that Jill is unable to go is $\frac{1}{5}$. Find the probability that (a) all arrive (b) just two arrive (c) only one arrives (d) none arrive.
   that (a) all arrive (b) just two arrive (c) only one arrives (d) none arrive.

10. Two boys are asked the days of the week on which their birthdays fall this year. Assuming any day is equally likely, find the probability of (a) both on a Sunday (b) both on the same day of the week (c) neither on a Sunday.

11. A box contains four plain and three milk chocolates. Three are drawn out and eaten. Draw a tree to show the possible results. What is the probability of (a) all the same kind (b) two plain and one milk (c) one plain and two milk.
    Check that your answers add up to 1.